GOLD IN THE GRASS

Rags to Riches Through Soil Reclamation
and Sustainable Farming

A Back-to-the-Land Adventure from 1954

Margaret F. Leatherbarrow

Norton Creek Press
http://www.nortoncreekpress.com

Gold in the Grass:
Rags to Riches Through Soil Reclamation and
Sustainable Farming

A Back-to-the-Land Adventure from 1954

Margaret F. Leatherbarrow

Originally published in 1954 in the U.S.A. by
Bouregy and Curl

ISBN 978-0-9721770-5-4

Norton Creek Press
36475 Norton Creek Road
Blodgett, Oregon 97326

http://www.nortoncreekpress.com

To my husband, Alfred, who made the writing of this story possible, and to our son, Jim.

INTRODUCTION

As World War II was ending, Alfred Leatherbarrow, a wounded Canadian veteran, and his nurse, Margaret, fell in love, married, bought their dream farm—and discovered that their crops would not grow. The farm's soil had been exhausted through years of destructive tillage practices.

Faced with certain defeat, they used innovative farming techniques—including a prototype forage harvester to gather grass for silage—to restore the fertility of their farm. This early experiment in sustainable agriculture not only saved the farm in a rags-to-riches turnaround, but showed other farmers in their region how to pull out of the death spiral of decreasing fertility, yields, and income.

Gold in the Grass is a love story, a back-to-the-land adventure, and an inspirational example of how conservation tillage can restore the fertility of a used-up farm. This is a great book, and has spent far too many of its fifty years out of print.

Gold in the Grass is an example of the Norton Creek Press motto: "Most of the best books are out of print and forgotten, but we can fix that!" Check out our offerings on http://www.nortoncreekpress.com.

Robert Plamondon
September, 2008

Alfred Leatherbarrow examining second-cutting alfalfa.

CHAPTER 1

At the time that this story begins, if one could say there is a beginning, Alfred was an ambulatory patient at Ste. Anne's Hospital, Quebec, awaiting surgery on his feet for *pes cavus*. He was lonely, disillusioned, restless, like a ship without a rudder. His academic education had come to a sudden halt; for at the age of fourteen this promising youth, always top in his classes, had had to become the breadwinner. His ambition had been to become a surgeon; and what a surgeon he would have made! He worked in the hungry thirties for $1.50 a week plus board, on a farm where he started work at 5 a.m. and continued till 9.30 p.m. Tough for a youngster, particularly when his quarters were cold, his clothes inadequate and there was no happiness in his life.

He had left Canada on the first boat train for overseas in 1939, disheartened and alone, with, in his own words, "A one way ticket." There was nothing to come back for. He had watched the familiar landscapes as the train sped through the area where he had spent his entire life, in and around Montreal.

Now that he was back, with an added 40 per cent physical disability, as well as no alteration in personal relationships, he was marking time, living from one day to the next with little interest. Perhaps when he got out of hospital he would buy a motorcycle and see Canada and the States. In the meantime a friend interested him in taking a course in navigation which, too, could lead to travel. There was not much to do but read, listen to the radio and await the operation which he hoped would take the pain out of his feet.

Margaret, the nurse, was trying her utmost to make her work all-sufficient, and failing miserably. Too much of her life had been spent living for tomorrow, which would surely be better than today.

1

It was late in the afternoon. Everything had gone wrong all day, and a vile humour held Margaret in its grip. The matron called, "Would you care to join a group of nurses going to Molson Stadium to hear the Montreal Symphony Orchestra tonight, with a group of patients?"

"I won't be off duty in time."

"You can leave early."

"All right."

"Seven o'clock at the main entrance."

"Fine." (Maybe the music will put me in a better mood, I (Margaret) thought.)

Alfred also picked up a ticket. He loved good music, and had never missed anything he had had a chance to hear overseas. The long trip would be impossible if he had to stand, so for protection he carried a book. He got in the bus early, to make sure of a seat, and settled down to read. Slowly it began to fill. Glancing up, he noticed the nurses standing near the entrance, and Margaret smiling and chatting with the others. Watching her, he thought, "There is the girl I'd like to marry."

Glancing at her hands to determine the obstacles in his way, he was foiled by gloves. The bus was filling rapidly; his nose returned to the book, and his mind to the girl he didn't see again until they stopped to get off. He waited at the exit, and followed Margaret across the campus, where the girls stopped to talk, before taking their places in the seats reserved for the Ste. Anne's party. He waited, hoping there would be an opportunity to sit beside her, but it looked hopeless, so he picked a seat in the second row, casting frequent glances toward the oblivious Margaret.

A little disgusted because the nurses had stuck together, instead of mixing with the patients, as she thought they were expected to, Margaret impatiently led the way to the seats; walked down the second row, and sat bang up against one of the patients. Two girls were wandering about aimlessly, Margaret thought. Leaning forward to see them better, she remarked, "They'll get lost. They don't know where the seats reserved for us are."

"Oh, they'll find them all right, don't worry." The soft voice sent shivers of ecstasy down her spine!

The music commenced, and we were transported into the realm of fantasy. A full August moon shone down from above. The ballet and the music of the Nutcracker Suite carried us through the evening like a song. Aware of each other's enjoyment in the music, conversation at intermission was easy. Suspicions and irritations vanished.

As the concert came to a close, the new friends sauntered back across the campus to the waiting bus, where Alfred found himself compelled to stand. He looked so tall, smiling down, that Margaret's heart did cartwheels. When the bus stopped at a restaurant for everyone to have coffee, conversation flowed freely between us, and there wasn't enough time to say what had to be said.

"When can I see you again?"

I had told him of the walk I liked to take down a farm lane, and how we called it Wilson's Walk. He would like to go down that lane with me.

"I have a half day tomorrow."

"Let us have a picnic."

Picnic it was. Walking hand in hand over a stubble field, eating our sandwiches in a fence corner, and finding there was still so much to talk about.

There were picnics in the rain and in the snow, bridge parties at the Lodge, and once a picture show. Alfred had his surgery on each foot at separate times, so that he was wearing a leg cast for most of the time.

November came, and leaning against a post of the veranda at the Red Cross Lodge, Alfred asked Margaret to marry him.

"Yes, yes," came a breathless reply, from one who had not dared to hope he'd ask her.

"If you are looking for someone to offer you success and money, do not marry me," he had said. "All I am interested in is enough security for a warm home, enough to eat and a comfortable bed."

Farming was his choice of occupation. Three years' experience at it before the war and a desire to have outdoor work increased this desire. Now he was going to have a wife, he couldn't wander.

"If I spend my entire life farming and finish up without any money, I will still have had a good life doing what I enjoy," he said.

On our way in to Montreal for an engagement dinner at his sister's, Alfred gave me a story to read in Reader's Digest called "My Ninety Acres", by Louis Bromfield. This, he feels, clinched farming for us as a career. He never quite believes me when I tell him I would have gone anywhere and done anything he wanted to at that time, and I have no reason to feel otherwise now.

The day of the first snowstorm, Alfred, on crutches, was determined to bind our engagement with a ring, and went in to Montreal for this purpose. He stood in Mappins' jewellery store leaning on his crutches for two hours, comparing rings, before he made his choice. I was terrified back at Ste. Anne's, knowing what he was doing and afraid he'd slip and fall; but there was no holding the man. A slight alteration in the size, plus some sentimental engraving, held the ring back for three days. Our favourite corner at the Lodge was occupied for this important ceremony, so he slipped it on my finger in the writing room, and I left immediately after to go on duty, walking in the clouds.

We were married January 5, 1946, quietly in a church, and left immediately for the station to board a train for Toronto.

The accumulation of years is bulky stuff to sort, pack and ship, some home, some to Toronto for use on our honeymoon, which was arranged through Daisy, a friend of mine. She had offered me her boathouse for the purpose, never dreaming I'd ask for it in midwinter.

I got everything packed and away but a pair of bulky snow boots I'd need for the winter in the bush. These I had to wear, and they could not have looked more incongruous, for there was no snow on our wedding day, just dull overcast skies. With a corsage on my coat and clodhoppers on my feet, I went with head in the clouds. In the vestry, before going to the altar, my cousin who accompanied me for this simple, solemn ceremony, asked, "Have you got everything, Margaret?"

"Yes, I've got Alfred," was the quick reply.

Everyone laughed; the tension was broken. The minister led us to the altar for our vows, from which nothing was

4

deleted, and in the name of the Father and of the Son and of the Holy Ghost, a simple gold band was slipped on my finger, never to be removed.

There was just time for brief good-byes to his sisters and brothers; then, with our witnesses, we taxied to Windsor Station. We made a grand entrance through the electrically opened door, had coffee in the restaurant, then boarded the train. Alfred had chairs reserved, and the porter tried to put us one at each end of the car. I suppose that is routine but it didn't work.

It was the shortest and the longest train journey from Montreal to Toronto I'd ever taken, and those chairs were still too far apart. "Rub-a-dub-dub, two men in a tub," sang the wheels over and over again, and we were there. Breakfast in our room in the morning took hours. We had a walk in the afternoon and went to Daisy's for dinner at night.

This was her first meeting with Alfred. Tomorrow she would start for Switzerland, and we for her boat-house in the bush, so she wouldn't know how we'd get along. No one had ever tried to stay there in winter. We had had a wonderful Christmas at his sister's where three families living in close proximity visited each other's Christmas tree ceremony, each family placing the gifts for everyone under their own tree. Alfred and I had a busy time putting gifts for each other under all the trees. One day while shopping together he had admired a display of raw wool sweaters in an exclusive men's wear shop. I went home, counted my money, again checking off what I had to get and could do without, and returning alone purchased the most expensive sweater I had ever bought, with a pair of socks to match.

Alfred was doing something similar, buying me fur mitts, warm pullovers and luxuries I wouldn't buy for myself.

We went into the bush well-equipped for cold and glad to be alone with each other. The few passengers of the small mail train made us feel that we were going into sparsely settled territory. The windows gave pictures of bushland, not too prosperous farm land by the look of the buildings on them, and glimpses of lakes covered with snow and ice. I made a list of supplies we would need, completely lost at this unaccustomed task. My confusion must have given Alfred moments of concern. I was really worried about how much all this was going to cost. Alfred had told me the exact extent of our finances, but I hadn't taken it in. All I could think of was, he was still on convalescent leave and with no profession to follow or job to go to; we'd better be careful of every nickel till we knew what was what.

Tom, the trusty handy man who looked after the place, met us with his jalopy. We stopped at a corner grocer's and spent forty-two dollars on food! Alfred picked up an iced cake.

"Here, this is the first and last cake I'll buy you," he laughed uneasily.

Four loaves of bread and yeast cakes I eyed, wondering if I'd ever master that art. Sugar was rationed then, and we were very careful of it, looking forward hopefully to the time when we would be settled in our own home and I'd be preserving and making jam.

I had described this boathouse to Alfred, having been there before. We bumped along, turned through a farmer's field, skirting the woods that lined the lake, then down a winding road through the woods past Daisy's big cottage, ice house, garage and tennis court to the little yellow and green boathouse. A cord of wood recently dumped beside it looked ominous.

Steps led to a porch opening into a red and ivory kitchen through which we could see a large room furnished in maple and panelled to match. Comfortable furniture was grouped round a large stone fireplace. A sunporch across one end faced the lake, and beside the kitchen was a bathroom, minus a tub or shower. There was a stove in the kitchen, and a fireplace in the living room, with water under the floor. This, then, was to be our home for the winter.

We had called at a farmhouse before turning in to the lake and made arrangements to buy eggs and milk, also pick up our mail, but chiefly to have a contact with civilization within walking distance; for when Tom drove away we were on our own. Conscious at last of how little we knew of one another, this would be the test.

I took Alfred's picture beside the wood pile. If it looked as bad to him as he looked incapable of coping with it in that picture, I was never made aware of it. We lit the fireplace and the stove and put the kettle on. It had a whistle and we called it "Percy."

I set the tea table, a handy little thing of painted blonde wood with drop leaves and wheels to slide it anywhere you wanted. Tea, toast, jam and cheese became an afternoon habit. Mexican pictures and ornaments and oriental rugs gave added warmth. It was cosy. Here we could forget the time of day, or even what week of the month it was. Hunger and heat were our only masters, and we were quite content to serve them.

We walked to the farm whose owner owned the wood lot skirting the road to the cottages, and asked if we could buy and cut some of the dead wood.

"Go ahead and help yourself. I don't know just what there is down there. You can have what you need."

This was a relief. That cord we had bought was, after paying for delivery, quite expensive, and when cut to size for use was disappearing fast into the jaws of our stove and fire-place. Alfred had cut wood three winters, as a boy in the woods of the Eastern Townships in Quebec, and enjoyed being a woodsman again. With a rusty old cross-cut saw he borrowed from the lean-to of a neighbouring cottage, carefully sharpened, and an axe, he set out to make a sleigh to haul the logs to the boat house. I watched and marvelled at his ingenuity and patience in searching out the exact pieces he wanted for the runners curved up in front.

Within two days, snow was falling heavily. No car could penetrate the bush now. But we didn't want one. It made us feel more secure in our solitude. Every day Alfred cut wood. Each time he was able to cut more than the day before. We found it advisable to turn the water off before the pipes froze, so modern conveniences were reduced to electricity. I found myself with distasteful household chores, but would not let on it bothered me. After all, we might be homesteading yet, and have worse to contend with.

It became bitterly cold. Alfred never let our supply of wood get low. The hungry fires were kept roaring day and night. Sometimes in the morning they would both be out, and I felt very pleased with myself when once I got up and lit the fires for Alfred.

After we had eaten two of the loaves of bread, we decided it was time to get out the cook book I'd bought for my trousseau. Together we kneaded the dough. It was exhausting work for muscles unused to a punching bag, but we kept right on following the directions to the letter, tiptoeing round the room when it was rising lest a heavy tread cause it to fall, and careful of drafts. At 2 a.m. the first loaves came out of the oven, beautiful golden brown works of art. Our mouths watered as the warm aroma filled the air, and we ate one large loaf between us before going to bed.

That was it! The last two Baker's loaves were stuck on sticks in the snow for birds. Were we ever proud of ourselves!

Trips to the farm for eggs and milk were made every other day. Alfred built a little tin toboggan from bits he'd found, to pull the groceries on, and from sketches I made, two pairs of snowshoes with twine for the mat. They were not bad for an amateur, and they did keep us from sinking in deep snow. By subscribing to a Toronto daily, we kept up with the outside world. Two days before we left we found out what was wrong with the radio that would give us one station only when it temperamentally felt like it.

This life was delightful; homesteading sounded attractive. There was considerable talk of British Columbia, where we would build a chicken house ourselves and live in it till we got going, then build a house. I visualized curtains for the windows with sun always streaming in.

One day in the midst of this idyll we had to go to Toronto for Alfred's checkup at Christie Street Hospital. The highlight of this trip was the shower bath. What luxury! Then we were glad to get back to the woods again.

No words can express the beauty of the moonlit nights and sunny days when the snow glittered like crystal and the sharp frosty air cut your nostrils, listening in the stillness to the cracking of dead wood, or watching a fox scurry through the woods. After one particularly bad storm the electricity went off, and we had a real hunt for an old oil lamp. The linesman summoned was very much surprised to find us living in the bush, and incredulous when we told him how long we had been there. Our farm friends had offered to take us to town any Saturday night we cared to go, but it had no attraction for us. We were content to see Fenelon Falls as a glitter of lights across the lake.

Early in March the snow vanished rapidly. It was an early spring, and little rivers threatened the destruction of the tennis court, giving Alfred a perfect opportunity to practice his engineering skill. No little boy ever got his feet wetter, or had more fun, and the tennis court was saved.

And then it was over, the honeymoon! Alfred had several more months of marking time, monthly visits to Christie Street, later to Westminster, to keep us from getting settled in a home of our own and an occupation. Farming was the choice. He had had a trade as a knitter in a hosiery factory, but preferred outdoor work. I could not bear to have Alfred at a job that necessitated punching a time clock. I wanted him to determine his own hours of work, and when and where.

We packed up. Our farm friends entertained us at dinner, and drove us to Lindsay. We gave them the sleigh and snowshoes. They were the only friends we had made in the two and a half months we had lived there. On now to Fergus and my people, whom Alfred had yet to meet. An ordeal for both of us, as I got laryngitis. Mother and Dad, both deaf, would help it not at all.

The family expected us. We took the evening train to Fergus where Kay, Larry, and Adeline, always on hand to do the right thing, greeted us. As we got out of the car at Broomfield, Adeline showered us with confetti, which startled an old married couple of over two months.

Mother looked tired and nervous. She was seeing a new son-in-law for the first time. She had to go to bed, and was ill for several days. I was plenty nervous myself.

Dad took Alfred to town in the mornings, and I tried to keep house. It must have been a hangover from childhood days when no one could cook as well as mother. I was as nervous as a kitten trying to have meals right on time. To put in time, Alfred tapped the maple trees circling the three-acre lot. Although it was a bit late in the season, he did very well; boiling the sap in boilers on a little stove we had had in the nursery as children, now relegated to the wash house, long since become a store room.

Sunday, the run was so good every available container held sap, and Alfred had to boil. Mother was horrified. Making syrup on Sunday—no good would come of it. Kay and Larry came up for the afternoon. Larry sat with Alfred sympathizing with his first run-in with Mother's rigid laws of behaviour. Alfred was unruffled. He took a saucer of delicious syrup up to Mother to taste, and her scruples vanished as she literally licked the saucer clean. Alfred was a pretty smart boy, if a little lax in Sunday observance, Mother thought, and soon rationalized his activity to a just occupation.

One Wednesday afternoon I walked down to Kay's with Alfred and never trod so long a block as the old familiar Main Street of my childhood. Between the Imperial Bank and the Post Office we met everyone I'd ever known, I think, and after more years than I'd like to state, their names evaded me. My confusion was not lessened as I remembered my reaction when I had asked Alfred his name before we got off the bus, the night we met so unconventionally. I laughed out loud. He should never have spoken to me again, laughing at a name so old that it can be traced back to the Norman Conquest of England, when Leatherbarrow meant Standard Bearer. But I had never heard it before. He got back at me. Now I watch the startled faces try to hide their giggles when I give our name.

We were restless, rested, healthy, and stronger. It was all right in the bush having no regular occupation, but living amongst people with definite hours to keep and jobs to do, and having none of our own, was no good.

Larry lent us his car and we visited farms for sale in the locality. Alfred had figured out just what he could afford to pay, and regardless of the attractive offer one farmer made him he would not deviate from what he could handle. We had an appointment to go before the Veterans' Land Act Board and make formal application for their assistance. In the meantime, Alfred decided he liked this part of the country. I think it was partly because he thought I'd like to be near my own people, and he and Mother were becoming fast friends.

Dad liked him all right too, till he turned down the farm Dad wanted him to buy.

We ran out of newspaper ads with one dilly near Brantford. The farm was advertised as "easily accessible, slightly rolling land in front, full line of equipment, new brick house, electricity," and the price listed was just right. It was Alfred's longest drive behind the wheel since coming home from overseas, and he was bathed in perspiration most of the day till our safe return—a nervous system not well adjusted yet.

The agent took us out. It was the first time he had seen it, too. The roads were terrible. We bumped and sank in frost boils, wondering if we would ever get back over the same road. At last the farm was in sight. The buildings were close to the road with no trees or shrubs to soften their dreary ugliness. The house was new all right, insul-brick. A good wind might tear it to pieces. A single light bulb dangled from the ceiling of each room. Equipment of a nondescript sort, weather-beaten and mostly useless, stood around in sad-looking barnyard neglect. The binder no doubt had not left its resting place in several years. We could just see it across the wide deep gully that had been described as "slightly rolling" but could not be worked, nor crossed any other way than by foot.

Finding a farm for our price on which we could live and make a way of life, looked pretty hopeless. We took our requirements to a local real estate agent and looked at a number of dismal places. March is no time to choose a farm, with nothing growing on it. At last, late one afternoon, we stopped at the house and barn of a place that had been uninhabited for two years. It looked terribly desolate. But it had promise, we thought. Getting the key from its owner, we gave the house a quick lookover. Its sloping ceilings upstairs and little steps from different levels where additions had been built at different times gave it an attraction that helped us to overlook the drawbacks we'd be bound to find in any old house. The barn, apart from needing a new roof, was well built, nicely laid out in the old conventional way with pig pens, chicken house, driving shed all combined and joined on to the run-in shed of the barn where box stalls were provided for horses and cows. It had a root cellar and a large cement water trough. There was even a goose pen near the chicken house steps. We would come back the following day and see the land and fences.

That night we called on the neighbours on either side to ask their opinion of the farm.

"Oh, it's good land, good land," they replied.

Satisfied, we figured this was it.

It was a cold bleak day, the day we gave it a thorough look-see. The agent and Alfred, both tall, strode on ahead, Dad and I trudging behind, till finally Dad went back and I had to catch up with the others. A wide sweeping gesture, taking in an unde-termined area, led us to believe the good fences were ours, or was it wishful thinking on our part? Alfred carried a shovel, digging it in frequently along the way to determine the type of soil.

Up over the high field we went, on down through marshy waste beside the cedar grove, worth a thousand dollars, the agent said, if only for shelter for the cattle. A spring which kept an old barrel full, never failing even in drought years, was worth another thousand. A tall straight elm that had become a landmark thereabouts, a farmer had offered $100 for, but the owner would not sell, as it might be useful to some future owners and incidentally improve the value of the farm that had suffered more than we knew in recent years. Hay had been sold off the farm, and it had been rented for pasture for two years. Commercial fertilizer had never been used. In other words, it was a farm gone to seed, producing weeds in abundance and nothing else.

We walked on up through the old pasture that had been cleared without thought of the value of a woodlot or conserva-tion, and now of little value; barren hummocks, and hollows with marshy areas and stone. Virgin soil this was. We passed through quickly and up the lane towards the barn, listening to amusing tales of hunting and trapping in the district. Pausing under a giant elm tree half way up the wide grassy lane, our agent told us the story of the hired man who had tried to commit suicide by shooting himself under this tree. The local doctor gave him the devil for not finishing the job, as now he was sure he'd be no good to himself or to any one else. But the man lived to marry and raise a large family.

Then there was a gravel pit at one side of a front field, that was worth a thousand dollars. Alfred took all these assets into consideration, but as to their value he kept his tongue in his cheek. Even the orchard, if for shade alone, was worth a thou-sand dollars!

The following day, the price having been agreed upon among the owner, the agent and Alfred, we had our appointment with the V.L.A. Board.

With what care I dressed and groomed myself that day! Anxious to appear strong, healthy, capable and sensible, knowing full well my contribution to farming could not possibly make it a good risk, I was depending upon personal appearance to carry me. Alfred, dressed immaculately in his blue serge suit, could very well have dispelled any idea these seasoned farmers on the board might have had that he could weather the years of hard work, long hours and, most likely, heartbreak. But they were kindly, when told of the farm we wanted and the terms we could get.

"Go ahead, take an option for three months, and your application will have gone through by then," we were assured.

"If it doesn't go through, I can get a mortgage, and we can do it anyway, if you like the farm," Alfred assured me.

"Sure I like it."

How could I say anything else? It suited Alfred, and I knew we could not start with everything perfect. I don't think I even wanted to. This way we would work together. Besides, I was terribly anxious to get into our own home, regardless of what it was like. We needed to be off from the crowd, alone together. Perhaps we were a little bushed. I think it was war experiences, too vivid still, that made peaceful secluded surroundings necessary for Alfred. And the long period of struggling with clashing personalities was not completely forgotten by me. We were impatient to begin our life together on this farm.

To make perfectly sure, an option for five months was taken, and the owner allowed us to move out to the farm immediately, although we would not be able to work the land until the rental term for pasture was up. There were the buildings, with plenty of work to be done on them. We were almost glad to have our entire time to devote to them. It would also give Alfred more time to shop around for stock and equipment. We were well satisfied with the arrangement.

I measured the windows and we spent a day in Guelph buying absolute necessities. First of all, a bed, the best we could buy in springs and mattress.

"After all, one third of your life is spent in bed. It might as well be comfortable," quoth Alfred.

Coal oil for the lamps Mother had donated from the wash house. Wash tubs and a wash board and boiler, brooms, mops, dust pan, pails, pots, pans. A plain wire toaster to hold over a coal fire was not to be had.

Neither could we get a bake board. People don't use them any more, I guess. But I didn't have a table yet. There was so much to do with our money we must be very careful of how it was spent.

Alfred brought Mother out one day. She peered in windows, climbed up the stable stairs to the barn floor, poked her head in everywhere. It delighted Alfred to see her interest. She said, "I was never in a barn before, and I don't believe Margaret has been either."

We swept the house, twice, untenanted for two years. Trivia that had not been disposed of at the sale lay about. A feather tick in the upstairs hall had been a nest for rats. An old rag stair carpet was torn from its staples, gathered up and burned with the feather tick.

On the kitchen floor were several different designs and colours of Congoleum under which lay rag rug and papers for insulation that made us wonder a little about winter. We knew, from the boathouse, what cold floors could be like. Nearly a bushel of tacks and staples was gathered up from the stairs and kitchen floor.

Now we were ready to move in and clean thoroughly. We did not own a car, and it was not practical to try to make the house livable just coming out daily.

CHAPTER 2

April 22, 1946, was a warm sunny spring day. A truck backed up to the veranda steps at Broomfield, and all our worldly belongings, which didn't consist of very much, were loaded on it. A chesterfield, two occasional chairs, a chest of drawers, and a coffee table. A large oval dining-room table that had been moving from home to home with the family, neither wanted nor needed by any of them, but kept because of sentiment; we could use it now, so it came with us temporarily. A bridge table, linen, bedding, dishes, silver. An old bedroom suite relegated long since to the wash house; this Mother thought of just before we were ready to leave.

"Take it, you might find a use for it some day, and it's no good here."

We drove out in the cab of the truck, with me clutching a bowl of cold boiled potatoes and a jar of marmalade.

"You won't want to bother cooking potatoes at noon," Mother said.

We stopped in Elora to buy groceries, having no idea just when we'd be back for more, or how we'd get there.

A visit to the telephone office earlier to arrange to have the telephone installed didn't promise anything immediate. There seemed to be shortages in everything, at the time we started to keep house.

We arrived at the farm about noon, concerned lest the truck from Guelph with our important purchases might have arrived before us. There were no tracks ahead of us, which was a relief, for our bed, consisting of a spring filled mattress and box springs, the best money could buy, would be on that truck. There would also be coal oil, for the array of lamps we had collected from the wash house.

"They will be along this afternoon," we thought. "No need to worry now."

All we wanted was to be alone in this our paradise.

The goods were quickly unloaded into the living-room; the trucker was paid and dismissed. What Alfred's thoughts were then, I don't know. I was a little frightened. Up till now, we had lived very comfortably with plans. This was their culmination, and now we were alone and stuck with it. The house lost its dreamer's glow, and looked as it really was, horrible and dirty.

We had planned a quiet way of life together, making a living doing what Alfred had long wanted to do. This he had dreamed of when lying in a slit trench overseas, not knowing whether he would get out of it alive. To own and operate a farm of his own the way he wanted! We had no idea, then, that it was the beginning of a career so fascinating, exciting, and useful that at the time of writing this, seven years later, we feel we are just beginning, in spite of the tremendous changes since it all began.

I was blissfully ignorant of all that being a farmer's wife involved, but anxious and determined to be the best possible partner.

We had arranged to buy milk and eggs from a neighbour until such time as we would have our own cows and chickens. We'd get along, we were sure. So today until our bed, coal oil, tubs, boiler, pots, pans, hoes, shovels and rake arrived, we'd enjoy our freedom in the sun.

Alfred built a fire in the ancient relic of a stove that had been left by the previous tenant, along with two decrepit chairs and a chimneyless oil lamp. The owner had suggested we buy this stove. We had so much that was old, and this thing, even with a fire going in it, was horrible. No, we would buy a new stove. The whole kitchen was a depressing sight. The floor, uncovered now, would need long hard hours of scrubbing. The walls were covered with a horrible dirty brown patterned wallpaper. Wainscoting and wood work were battleship grey. Windows were too dirty to let much light in. There was a sad lonely looking lampshelf, with a dirty white curtain that we had forgotten to burn hanging from it. It did not look inviting enough to have our first meal in. The living room was no better.

Fortunately, the sun was shining and it was a warm day. The bridge table set up on the back veranda and the two rickety chairs looked more attractive. Here we ate dinner; cold ham, fried potatoes, bread and marmalade, and tea. That reminded us of the well, long in disuse; until we had a report on the sample sent for analysis, all water would have to be boiled. We hoped we were "blessed with good water."

I gathered up our dishes and proceeded to wash them at the sink, a black cast iron affair with a wood sill about four inches wide, enclosed with a little door that didn't stay shut. But the pump worked. Not very modern, but running water in the house, even if not for drinking purposes, was an asset.

We had never looked in the sink. As it was black and in a dark windowless corner, we had taken what we expected of it for granted.

"Alfred, there is no outlet," I exclaimed.

This, then, was to be the first improvement in the house; but we had to get to town to buy a piece of pipe first.

"Let's go fishing," said Alfred to a willing wife.

He hunted up some fish hooks and string. Turning our backs on the house, and the problems, real and otherwise, that loomed before us, we wandered down the lane hand in hand, drawn irresistibly to the grassy bank of the little stream that skirted the western end of our property. We had been assured there were trout in it (worth another $1,000!).

Here we lay in the sun, unaware of nibbles on the line, if there were any, drunk with the quiet peacefulness of our sur-roundings. We could see the house and lane, certain that we would also hear a truck approach.

Why do tradesmen promise to send your purchases by truck on a specified day when they have no intention of doing so? Ours came, three days later by train to the nearest railway station, two miles away.

It was getting on in the afternoon when we realized that our idyll must come to an end. We'd have to get busy and fix up a bed. Mother's donation to the cause was going to be useful sooner than we thought. With no oil for our lamps, we'd have to go to bed before dark.

Our situation was too funny to be tragic. Besides, we each had to show the other we were made of stern stuff. Alfred suf-fered most. He is over six feet tall, and the springs weren't long enough, so that his ankles rested on the hard wood of the frame. Our seats touched the floor, in spite of having the springs elevated as high as all the bricks we could find to support them would allow. We would have slept on the floor with more comfort, but it had to be scrubbed. Each of the three nights we spent this way we were sure would be the last.

The station agent, unable to reach us by phone, had to send a letter. Alfred had to find a trucker. Without a telephone or car, this was not too easy. From a neighbour, we heard of a man who lived on a farm near the station. Alfred set out across the fields. It was noon, and he was determined we would have a bed to sleep on before night. The two bachelors, one being the trucker, were just finishing their dinner, so Alfred sat and waited. The trucker wiped his plate with a piece of bread, which he ate; then, after wiping the plate with a piece of newspaper, he turned it upside down on the table ready for the next meal, and the two men set off for the station.

The Old Boy was very interested, and regaled Alfred with neighbourhood news. When they arrived back with our purchases, they were talking like old friends.

Every other day I crossed the fields with a quart bottle for milk, and also got eggs if we needed them. It was pleasant to chat for a few minutes with a farm wife; watch her at the homey occupations of a busy life, caring for the home, chickens and dairy. I liked the feeling of partnership this type of life would give me with Alfred, and grew impatient to be doing all these things, washing separators, gathering eggs or caring for the baby chicks. I watched her sew patches on her husband's overalls, and felt impatient to do the same for Alfred; his were so new and unworn yet.

I was full of enthusiasm when Alfred suggested, and later shopped around for, a cow. Black Maggie and her bull calf soon kept the grass in the orchard short. Alfred set to work digging a large garden, trimming gooseberry bushes. I started upstairs to scrub each room, dreading the time when there would be nothing for it but to scrub the kitchen.

Eleanor, my sister-in-law, came out and took us to a sale in Elora. Here we bought, quite reasonably, furniture that we needed. I had not learned yet not to admire or even suggest wanting something. A Governor Winthrop desk caught my eye and Alfred noticed it. We bought a bedroom suite for six dollars, dining room chairs, tables, equally cheap. The table, still in use in the kitchen, fell to us for 75 cents.

Eleanor had to get home, so she took me back to the farm, and Alfred stayed till the last to get our friend the trucker to bring our treasure home.

Thinking of the purchases, and how they would add i homey touch to the bleak house, I felt well pleased, particularly over the dresser for our bedroom. It had a lice big bevelled mirror, with no out-of-date curlicues an its frame. This, in a light maple colour, with just the head of the bed used, would make the beginning of in attractive bedroom.

Then Alfred and the Old Boy arrived; their faces long.

"We've had an accident."

"What happened?"

"The mirror of the dresser was on top of the cab. It fell off as we came down the hill and smashed."

Alfred watched me as I stifled my disappointment. When he moved the desk forward to take it off the truck, I was able to forget the mirror temporarily, in the pleasure I felt at getting a desk which was a real luxury.

"I was offered the price I paid for it before the sale was over, but I thought you wanted it."

"Darling, thanks!"

We put an oval mirror over the dresser and told each other, "That looks much nicer."

Two days later, about dinner time, the Old Boy arrived with a sideboard he'd picked up somewhere, with the most impossible mirror, all blotches.

"I felt so bad your losing that mirror that I brought this over in case you wanted it."

We paid two dollars for the atrocity rather than hurt the man's feelings, and asked him to stay for dinner.

Up till now, three orange crates, draped with a white and black polka-dotted curtain were my only cupboard. Alfred took the mirror and bric-a-brac off the dresser, and it gave me a place for the china I'd kept piled on the table in the living room till now. Besides, we were going to start decorating the living-room and I'd have to find a place for a lot of things that covered the old oval table.

A neighbour had lent us his car to go to town to order a kitchen stove. We had been wise not to buy the old relic. I'd not been able to get the oven hot enough to warm dishes, so I couldn't practise my meagre art of cooking to the full on Alfred, yet. We'd had one valiant effort, the last day it was used. Dinner was in progress when a sudden roar made us jump from our seats and run outside. The heat given forth from the stove, as I passed, made me think:

"I'll bet that oven's hot now."

A glance told me it was. Outside, we watched flames streak heavenward from the chimney as we stood helpless below. There was no ladder on the place; no way of getting anything up there to douse the flames. The roof was dry. There had been no rain for some time. All we could do was watch. Perhaps the intensity of our thoughts granted us our fervent wish. The fire subsided and no damage had been done. The oven cooled quickly, so no cake or biscuits were baked either. So the old stove was moved in front of the west window, and a newer shiny model took its place.

Finishing his dinner, the Old Boy looked sidelong at the old stove.

"She wants me to pick it up. You certainly don't want it sitting round here in your road, so I'd better just take it along today. It's not much use any more."

"We'll say it isn't!"

They measured the stove and the doors and found a problem on their hands. It was too big to get out the door in one piece. All the nuts and bolts were rusted. There was nothing for it but a hammer and cold chisel. Each time it was struck with the cold chisel, a piece of the casting came off.

We stood by, watched and listened, as he painstakingly tried to take it apart, and it continued to resist. A steady monologue increased in tempo with the hammer blows.

"It isn't any good, it never was any good; you had to sit on top of it to get any heat. Mr. — says it was never any good." And, with the crash of the hammer he literally smashed it to pieces.

"It's only junk," he cried, and when he finished with the hammer, that is exactly what it was.

We were convulsed with laughter to see this mild old man take matters decisively into his own hands and destroy a use-

20

less stove that did not belong to him, then pile it on his truck and take it to the gravel pit. At least its last resting place would be on the farm where it had been useful.

The kitchen looked almost beautiful with the shiny new stove. I vowed I'd keep it polished! The sink had been made useful, too. I could pour water in, and it would run right away. Wonderful, wonderful. My Alfred could do anything.

Now came the telephone. An old friend of my family's came to install it. Everything was going to be just perfect. The bread man called twice a week, and brought groceries and meat if we wanted him to. I was so afraid of food spoiling that I bought perishables with great care. We were out of meat, just two strips of bacon there were, until the bread man came in the afternoon.

"If I could have my dinner here, it would save a lot of time. Of course, I can go into Elora," he said.

What could I do?

"Of course, you can have your dinner. There isn't much," I apologized. "But, if you don't mind, you are quite welcome."

I dressed up the bacon, scrambling eggs and cutting the bacon in, and thought no more about it.

During this time, Alfred and I were working steadily at getting the seven layers of wallpaper off the living room. Fortunately, the floor didn't matter too much. We sloshed water on by the pailful, and scraped till our arms ached. If we got a strip two feet long off at one time we felt we had really accomplished something. This was, by far, not the worst we encountered. Alfred used five pounds of putty filling in cracks and holes in the wood work alone. It took every bit of his time all day for three weeks to plaster cracks and holes where we had taken out six inch spikes that must have held ponderous portraits of ancestors. It would have been much better to have had the room plastered, but that was not on our budget. Instead, Alfred wore the skin on his fingers so thin that they were extremely painful for weeks after. Then we painted the woodwork a nice ivory.

The family, sorry for our plight and curious, came out every Sunday afternoon, and couldn't see much improvement. Mere words couldn't impress them with the tremendous task we'd undertaken, and how long it was taking to do it. I think they thought we were going to be shiftless, and here we were working longer, harder hours than any of them. Perhaps I was too sensitive, or aware of the contrast between their homes and ours; afraid Alfred would be self-conscious about it. Anyway I dreaded their visits, and finally dropped a hint that stopped them coming every Sunday.

We needed more shelf space in the kitchen, now the dining-room table had to be cleared for action, so the boards from the granary were built into rough shelves where one day we intended having an electric stove. They could not be cut, as we would need them in the granary next year. The table was all we had to cut and paste wallpaper on. I pictured the former owner, now deceased, turning over in his grave at such desecration of the old heirloom. We would take good care of it, however, because it was the only table we would have for some time, to use for parties, or swanking, by serving dinner in the dining alcove of the living-room, now taking on a new look.

It was a pretty large room, 26 feet long, 18 feet wide, with all those windows, an archway, and doors to cut paper for. We were hesitant, both novices at paper hanging, with visions of being wound up in the stuff before we were done. Alfred inquired around about paper hangers. A woman was recommended, and on May 23, in the evening, she called to say that she could come the following day.

Stuck again, I had two pork chops. Alfred and the diminutive dynamo worked together in the living-room and their lively conversations and laughter continued throughout the day.

I cut the meat from the bones of the chops and camouflaged the small serving of meat, hoping they'd be finished before supper, which they weren't. It was nine o'clock when all was finished and we stood in the lamplight admiring the clean, new room.

"It's the nicest paper I've put on in a long time," she said.

Alfred's final visit to Christie Street Hospital brought his convalescent discharge and a transfer to the district of Westminster Hospital for periodic checkups as a pensioner.

We bought the floor covering then, and a number of little household necessities. A mail order catalogue had been of no use. How well I remember the day when, after poring over its pages, we wrote out an order for two hundred and forty dollars worth of merchandise. We waited with keen anticipation for such items as a wire toaster and a bake board that never came. Our order sheet was returned with twelve dollars of merchandise, consisting chiefly of four kitchen chairs. The table was unavailable, and so was most everything else. Alfred was furious.

"Why in hell do they put out a catalogue if they can't fill the orders?" he raged and, wrapping up the big book, mailed it back with a hot letter to the firm that issued it.

A very apologetic letter mentioning "the shortages since the war," with a few more items we'd purchased to bring our total to sixteen dollars, came in short order.

So, whether we had to or not, we were going to do without a lot of things we had considered essential.

Alfred made me a toaster with a nice long handle that would hold one piece of bread down through the stove lid, if the fire were low. He also made a bake board which I still use. One Sunday evening, as we were finishing supper, Mary Dass, a lifelong friend of mine, telephoned.

"Mother wants to come out to see you. Will you be home for a little while?"

"Yes, of course. We'd love to see you."

"Then we will come right away."

I had taken Alfred to call on them one day while we were waiting to get a farm, just as I would have taken him to my grandmother had I had one living.

Mrs. Dass was crowding the century mark, a remarkable old lady whom I'd thought of as my grandmother and visited as far back as I could remember. It was an honour to have her call on us. They came; she sat on a straight chair just inside the door, her ability only to distinguish little more than light from dark did not dim the courage of this indomitable spirit.

"My, your home is lovely, Margaret, I'm so glad to see you in your own home. That archway is so pretty."

We all sat there, lumps in our throats. The room was bare, only the new paper and paint gave promise of attractiveness.

"She isn't well and should not be out, but we couldn't stop her. She's been determined to see you in your own home ever since you moved out here," Mary whispered.

We were sitting on the chesterfield at one end of the empty room. After they left, we found that Mrs. Dass had put a substantial wedding present on the chesterfield. It was her last visit anywhere; the last time she left her own home till her death a year later. In the hearts of all who have known her she lives immortal.

CHAPTER 3

We knew that this farm was to be ours, regardless of what the Veteran's Land Act people decided about our qualifications. How we loved each Sunday to walk hand-in-hand over the fields, searching out the fence corners long overgrown with untrimmed shrubbery. Man, grown tired, had left this bit of earth for nature to take over. Hawthorne was creeping in, golden rod and thistles had literally taken over. We didn't see this picture then in its true light, but were impatient to plough the soil and sow grain, visualizing a bounteous golden harvest, nature's reward for long hours of toil.

Alfred contented himself by planting the large garden, long straight rows of carrots, beets, beans, onions, lettuces and radishes. Tomato plants were set out in perfect formation, so that no matter from which angle you looked the stakes were in a straight row. He taught me how to prune the plants and tie them as they grew to the tall stakes, and now to thin the vegetables when they were up enough to hoe.

"Man, that's a beautiful garden you've got," Dad said when he visited us, and we were justly proud.

Alfred asked the man who had rented the farm for pasture if he could plough up a couple of acres on the south side of the house for potatoes and corn.

"Sure, go ahead; you can let your couple of cows pasture too, if you wish."

He sat in the kitchen, a round brown felt hat tipped forward on his head, and the chair tipped back, telling us all about the occupants of the farm for years back. It was nice to get the history of the place and its people, making us feel that we had known it always, and belonged.

The neat work bench in the garage gave character to its former owner, till he became a friendly companion whose ire we almost felt when drastic changes were wrought as the years rolled by. Upstairs an L-shaped room that had previously been a hallway till the kitchen and two bedrooms were built on, we called the ghost walk. Here, Alfred liked to tell the children who visited us, walked the ghost of Billy, who did the chores every full of the moon. Or, when the wind blew and the rafters creaked, "Old Billy's up again." A friendly ghost we manufactured for our own amusement. The dark hallway became a catch-all for things we didn't know what to do with and hated to throw out just yet. We gave the place warmth with our imaginings and continuity through the lives lived here before we came.

The golden rod and thistles ceased to be a sign of neglect and desertion; even the burdock in the orchard was friendly until its burs ripened in the fall to plague us. A neighbour loaned his team and plough, and I watched Alfred, long-unaccustomed to this task, work with determination to turn the sod. His long legs strode behind the plough, pain shooting up his legs with every step. Only his tight lips told me how it hurt.

We bought good seed potatoes, three bags of them, and I sat under the crab-apple tree, cutting them for planting. I couldn't have been slower, examining each potato for the most strategic cut. "Three eyes to a piece," Alfred said. We planted them. Alfred with the hoe, I with a pail of cuts to drop in the specified place. I wished I'd been built closer to the ground before that operation was finished. More beans and peas and corn. "Mother and I canned corn one year and made a nice profit," Alfred said. We bought a canning machine in anticipation.

Cattle roamed the farm now. Our fortress fence too soon became inadequate. There isn't anything more curious than a cattle beast. They just have to know every nook and cranny where they graze. Alfred patched and mended the old slat and wire fence, till it looked like an entanglement, and we were sure nothing could get through. Or was that wishful thinking?

Neighbours began to call. They all knew, via the grapevine, the arrangement under which we were living here. Farm help, particularly for short term jobs was impossible to get, so Alfred in the vicinity was a godsend. Before our visitors would get down to the business of their neighbourly call, an almost set routine of topics, designed to get the most information, would be discussed, commencing with the weather which we have always with us, and good for fifteen to twenty minutes discussion. This I can understand, since from the beginning of time the farmer has been at its mercy; an enemy he depends on for his very existence. Yet now, with radio and a remarkable weather bureau to guide us, how many farmers have found the weather their friend? How often have we heard it said.

"On July 1st I cut my hay. If the weather is uncertain, that's my tough luck."

We started farming with no hide-bound rules to follow. We didn't do things because our fathers and grandfathers before us had done thus and so. It proved to be our greatest asset.

So the weather, our ancestry and that of our neighbours duly cared for, the crucial question came.

"Could you help us for a few days, or weeks?" as the task demanded. "Of course," said Alfred, willingly, "I'd be glad to."

He charged that summer fifty cents an hour from the time he arrived at the farm for work, not counting the hour for meals.

It was good to meet the country folk and know who your neighbours were, asking questions about the agricultural practices of the district, learning what to expect by seeing the fertility and production of the land and practices of those about us. On one place he worked, the two men brought in fifty loads of hay in fifty hours.

We were doing more on the farm now, anxious to make good use of our facilities as well as time. We had twenty-one weanling pigs for the large pig pen, to take care of the skim milk. I was terribly excited when they arrived, and insisted on helping unload them, carrying the squirming squealers by a hind leg from truck to pen. Later, I assisted Alfred by holding each one that had to be castrated, while he performed with sure surgical skill that unkind but necessary operation. Watching his slender long fingers work rapidly and efficiently I wondered, "Had he had the opportunity, would he not have been a great surgeon?"

Being a farm wife, I must have chickens but felt somewhat timid about my ability. There seemed to be such a lot to do for them, and they looked so tiny when I visited next door and watched my neighbour caring for the baby chicks.

We ordered fifty pullets and fifty cockerels from a hatchery we knew nothing about, except that its name was attractive. I had put the wedding present money in the bank in a special account, and on my insistence, to be used to buy poultry and necessary equipment. The house was not settled enough to be sure what we would really like to spend that money on. In poultry we could increase it and later buy more for the house with the profits. Oh yes, we counted our profits away ahead.

The pullets arrived at the station and Alfred had to borrow a car to get them. It was terribly exciting. We had bought them six weeks old this time, it being late in the season and warm enough not to need to purchase a brooder stove.

The boxes emptied carefully into the chicken house, I couldn't even touch them, and I knew some day I'd have to.

A letter had come to say the cockerels would be delayed, as they had developed a slight case of coccidiosis.

"What's that?" we inquired of each other. Looking at the little feathered charges I now had, sick ones I could not face. We cancelled the order, and I settled down to read all the books and pamphlets we had received from O. A. C. on chickens. There are volumes. It made me dizzy thinking of all the diseases they were susceptible to. If I raised a quarter of these, I'd be lucky. Everyone about us had lots of chickens, so I inquired about their methods of feeding, amounts, etc. Perhaps my approach was wrong, or I had committed an unpardonable offence. I got a brushoff so pointed that it startled me.

"We get a special feed you would not be able to obtain," helped me not at all.

Raising chickens then was our problem. To arrive at the proper method, we'd have to figure it out for ourselves.

"Alfred, I hope if the day ever comes when someone asks us how we do something, that we will have the decency to tell them," I said. I was sizzling. That that day would come, we were not aware could be possible, yet it did.

I don't believe I lost more than three or four chickens. Later, when the days were warmer still, I placed a board across the three steps to the chicken house and shoved them out for sunshine and fresh air, shoving them back at night with equal concern. Every one of them, left to themselves and without the gang plank could have found their way in and out all day, and returned at night to roost. The work ignorance makes for herself is tremendous. But I was happy proving my worth! And Alfred got a great kick out of watching me.

When the hens began to lay, it was terrific! I hardly gave them a chance to sit on a nest, running down every half hour to see if one had laid another miracle. Nor will I ever forget the first basket of eggs I took to the grading station. I went into town with a neighbour, walking over with my basket of eggs, far more wonderful to me than the three thirty-dozen crates she had piled around us in the car. The poor girl who did the counting had to do mine immediately. I just had to see the grade I got and how much interest on our investment we'd made.

We started to paint the outside of the house a cheerful white with red trim to look warm in the winter and clean in the summer. I've always wanted to take the brush from a painter I might be watching, and do the fascinating job myself. Being the painter, responsible to get the job done, is entirely different. Then, it can grow tedious and tiring, particularly if you have the unimaginative decorations on our veranda to paint that I had. Every square foot with five holes that had to be painted inside. Whoever designed it must have thought five the lucky number when rolling dice.

Alfred was away from early morning till late at night working on neighbouring farms, hoeing turnips and bringing in the hay. He thought my progress very slow, which it no doubt was. I didn't know there was lots and lots I could do besides paint, with two acres of beans, peas, corn and potatoes to weed, as well as the kitchen garden. Seeing my anxiety to please and be truly useful, Alfred would hide his irritation, but he must have wondered just how useless I was really going to be.

There were taut moments of misunderstanding when our limitations were not truly understood by each other, or we were tired. Alfred worried more than I knew. He realized, what I was oblivious of, that even with the V.L.A. help we were faced with a big undertaking, and not much to finance it. He knew also that he had not half the strength and staying power he had had before the war. It had been suggested that he work at something that would keep him off his feet.

"What do you want me to do, drive a taxi?" he had replied.

That occupation, though a good one, was as foreign to his nature as anything could be. The soft earth should be easier than anything. He'd give it a good try, and stick it out if at all possible. How often he felt he couldn't, I will never know.

His face, drawn and grey with fatigue as he trudged home each evening, silenced my voice if he was irritable at seeing how little I'd accomplished; and with a new day I'd put greater effort into my unaccustomed task.

Alfred never asked for a task that would save his feet when working on the other farms. He would ask endless questions about the farm practices, storing up ideas for his own use. Two years later, one of the men he'd worked with this first summer remarked,

"I wondered whether you didn't know anything, or else an awful lot." Who you are, or were, and what you did previously soon become common knowledge in the country, and the inevitable had to happen sooner or later. I was perched on the veranda roof, hanging on for dear life with hands and feet, while trying not to miss a spot, painting the eaves. Alfred was near the front of the house, and I could hear the voices, but not what they were saying. It was a man asking to speak to me.

"What do you want to see her about?" queried Alfred.

"She's a nurse, isn't she?"

"No, she's a housewife. Well, she did nurse."

"I want her to nurse my mother."

"Sorry, she won't. She is a farm wife now."

"I'd like to ask her."

"Go ahead, but you are wasting your time."

He was. I was perched, as I said, on the roof in paint-spattered overalls. Maybe I didn't care for what I was doing, but I didn't care to go back to the profession I had left. This new one took all my time, interest, and energy. It was against all the training I had received to say "No," but from my lofty height easier to say it, which I did. I was thankful that Alfred did not want me to nurse. He often said,

"If you want to nurse, I'll stop work. There is no use having more than one wage earner. I can sit on a chair all day on the veranda, and smoke."

He wanted to provide for me, and most of all he wanted me to be willing to live on what he could provide. This I liked and honoured. Money, though very necessary, must never be all important to us. Our love, our life, and all our worldly goods, in that order, must be guarded as priceless possessions the way we saw fit; any little irritation or fancied wrong quickly forgotten by playing a game. Which one could be first to get enough equilibrium back to say, "I'm sorry," regardless of how justified he felt?

The stove that I intended to keep a shining jewel and failed miserably to do! One day we were going to pick wild strawberries. Alfred went on ahead while I cleaned the stove. Again I was so slow his irritability mounted as the minutes passed, and when I did appear, all innocence, the storm of irritation broke, and for quite some time we gathered berries keeping far apart, each nursing a justified anger, oblivious of the beautiful day, the trees and rolling land, so warm and sweet smelling. At last, I could not stand it any longer and rushed to his waiting arms blind with tears and contrition. Without that oneness, so precious to us both, the farm and our lives were empty useless things.

Beth wrote she'd like to visit us over the first of July. We had worked together at Ste. Anne's. She had left before I did. What fun it was getting out the white linen bedspread I had decorated with Italian cut work in my dreaming days, and hand-knit linen lace. It suited the old-fashioned room with the pink and green bedroom china. A trumpet vine outside the window added atmosphere, and a little vase of old-fashioned flowers from the garden gave it friendliness.

I met her at the gate when her taxi brought her out. It was easy for her to see my happiness. So, no matter how the house looked, even to Beth, it held warmth, friendship, and love. We had a real visit, talking ourselves out, lying in the sun or walking over the fields. The next time Beth came was with her husband several years later.

One day when Alfred and I were working in the field on our "cash crop" we heard a bullet whizz perilously close. We were startled, being unaware anyone was hunting, or that any person but ourselves was on the farm.

"They must think there is still no one living here," Alfred called to me, as he ran to the fence to wave and warn the hunter we were there. The hunter saw him all right, so Alfred returned to work feeling quite safe; until a few minutes later another bullet ricocheted so close I was terrified.

With one bound Alfred leaped the fence and brandishing a stout stick, tried to cut the hunter off, as the latter, who had been shooting illegally from his car, hurriedly drove away.

"I didn't spend five and a half years in Europe during the war to come back here and be shot by a damn fool hunter," Alfred exclaimed.

He was furious. Had he been able to get close enough to get the car license, there would have been court action. Hunters of this type, and there are far too many, are a menace to the community. In the seven years we have been here, only two hunters have asked permission to cross our property, and there have been too many instances like the first one. We felt the time had come to prohibit shooting on the farm; we were sorry, but it just had to be done.

I carried on with the house painting, with Alfred away much of the time. Often I could see him working in a neighbouring field and we would signal to each other by flinging out our arms, then hugging them to us. A lovely signal, expressing all we felt for one another, and if at the moment we felt oppressed, our greeting brought us close and dispelled all doubts and fears. Together, we could tackle anything.

Three months had gone with an occasional visit from the V.L.A. field man, to whom we talked freely of our aims with a confidence he must have marvelled at. I don't remember his name now; he looked very immaculate in our humble kitchen, quite out of place in fact. He must have felt our task here not humanly possible, but never said so, just listened to our plans related with great enthusiasm by us both.

We were beginning to wonder when the V.L.A. people were going to let us know whether our application had been decided upon. The roof on the barn had to be attended to. Good weather would not last indefinitely; besides, priorities we could get through the V.L.A. might make materials more difficult to obtain on our own. Finally, Alfred felt he could wait no longer. If the V.L.A. people had not held him up so long, he could have got steel for the roof at least, so the local firms assured him. They had had plenty early in the season; now there was nothing. So it was decided not to wait any longer, but put on the new roof if we could get anything with which to do it.

Alfred went to a wholesale house in Kitchener, where probably for the first and last time he used his war record as a stepping stone.

"If the V.L.A. people hadn't held me up so long, I would have been able to get enough steel to do it. Now I can't get a damn thing," he explained. Whereupon the man nibbled on his V.L.A. bait.

"Oh, are you a veteran?"

"Yes, six years service."

"What branch?"

"Army."

A pause, the man looked quizzically at Alfred and cautiously asked, "Overseas?"

"Five and a half years."

Alfred had been told they only had fifty-eight squares of asphalt shingles, and he wanted fifty-two!

"We can only sell ten to a customer," they said.

"What the hell can I do with ten squares, when the whole barn has to be roofed?"

War experiences were swapped for a little while, and Alfred walked out with a receipted bill for fifty-two squares, to be delivered next day. The prize for five and a half years overseas was the privilege of putting a new roof on his barn!

Now came my first experience in feeding a bunch of hungry men. A local man took on the roofing job. Some days there would be four, some seven men. I rarely knew until they arrived how many there would be. That didn't matter a great deal. Servings of meat perhaps had to be a little less, so if they couldn't warn me ahead of time it was they who suffered. However, I tried to keep posted on the number to cook for and had been assured on Saturday there would be only four. Fine! I had nice Swiss steaks. Daisy and Norman were coming for their first visit; she wasn't long back from Switzerland. I was busy trying to get everything ready for dinner, and the house shining before our guests would arrive. Looking out the window I counted, not four, but seven men. I called our butcher. Would he give the postman a roast of beef for me?

"Sure."

"So with the mail came a roast of beef—late, but we would have our dinner after the others. The kitchen table would only seat four comfortably and I was putting seven around it as it was. This once, no man would get his elbows even near the table.

Daisy, unprepared, because of my glowing happy letters, arrived in time to help peel potatoes—enough, she thought, for a week. I put my nice white damask cloth on the oval table, which had been moved around until we felt it stood in the spot that would give our dinner guests the most pleasant view. There wasn't much choice as far as the room was concerned, but each window held a picture of the rural landscape, unsurpassed for beauty.

The Swiss steaks I put on a large platter in the centre of the table for each man to help himself; the vegetable had to be served from the stove. The roast cooking in the oven smelled good, and tasted quite as good as the steaks I had intended for us. I hoped there would be enough left for Alfred and me the following day.

CHAPTER 4

In order to get his re-establishment credits of over $1,000, and be in a position to take up our option on the farm, Alfred had to cancel the V.L.A. application. We now went ahead with the legal business of purchase—title searching, finding someone to take a mortgage—all very serious and businesslike. Finally, with the farm in joint ownership, I felt terribly important and responsible. When all the details were completed, we had a farm with a mortgage of two thousand dollars, and fourteen hundred dollars to stock and equip it. Not much as prices were in 1946, but enough to call for a celebration. We were people of property, landowners, independent. We were rich in our own minds—and is there any wealth greater than freedom to plan and live your life as you see fit.

We borrowed a car for a pleasure trip and a game of bridge at Broomfield. Past the age when man is full of his importance, Mother and Dad delight in a good game of bridge and will listen with understanding patience to us when we can talk of nothing else but what we are, or are going to do. This was our celebration.

The day our names were affixed to the deed of sale, we needed to talk. Later, a good night's sleep, and perhaps some minor mishap round the farm, would bring us back to grim reality.

Maggie, the cow, had been joined by Lily and Helen —two Jerseys. Helen was a heifer bred to a beef bull and Alfred was concerned lest she have trouble delivering her first calf. We let her roam the farm with half a dozen steers we dubbed "The Boys" in close attendance at all times. Lily argued it out with Maggie, who had a more placid nature, and became head of the herd. The steers were the scourge of our existence that first summer. I soon lost all fear of them. I had learned how comical such fears were, when I first encountered livestock in numbers on our honeymoon.

There was a field through which the road to the cottages passed. Some distance away stood a barn, as far as I knew uninhabited. One day when passing through the field to the farmhouse for our mail, I discovered a herd of Aberdeen Angus cattle peering at me from the corner of the barn, and thought nothing of it till curiosity got the better of the cattle. With one accord the thundering herd bore down on defenceless terrified me, caught midway between fences.

"Alfred, Alfred!" I called, feeling my last moment had come. Someone had told me never to run, but to remain calm, to walk, or better still to stand motionless, if runaway horses started to follow. As a child I lived near a spur line to the mill, and runaway horses were a traffic hazard. Perhaps this advice pertained also to cattle. I didn't know, but not daring to turn, I could almost feel their hot breath on my neck as I walked steadily to the gate that seemed so far distant.

The farmer's wife said she thought I might be afraid of the cattle, but that they would not hurt me. I didn't quite believe her as I courageously turned back with the mail, hoping at best to be able to die in Alfred's arms. Alfred was quite amused about my lengthy hair-raising tale, and there was nothing for it but to continue braving these beasts; but if I died beneath their hoofs, then my fears would be justified!

That was in my tenderfoot days. Now I was a seasoned farmwife, at least in chasing cattle.

We would be at Broomfield for bridge and coming home, as we started in the house, one or other of us would stop and listen, and say, "I hear cattle in the corn."

Then the race would begin. We would run blindly unless there happened to be a moon, following the sound of breaking cornstalks or a munching steer.

Shouting like Indians, we would tear madly after them; the distance we'd chase them depending on the extent of our anger. I generally stopped halfway up the hill, beyond the low land behind the barn. Needless to say, the steers got all that cash crop of corn. We didn't even get any for our own use. It wasn't any good anyway, and that was serious.

The beans and peas planted here, lost in weeds, were found by the unerring skill of the cattle. One night I wakened to the sound of strange noises outside our window and finally roused Alfred. He beamed the flashlight out the window and caught two wide eyes gazing up from the centre of the tomato plants. One of the "Boys" had developed a definite taste for tomatoes. He broke the stakes and trampled the plants, until what we could rescue of the tomatoes were gathered. Alfred threw the axe at him one day; fortunately he missed.

I don't think we would have done too badly as cross-country sprinters after the practice we had that summer. The house and orchard became a frequently attacked fortress. We began inquiring at what date we could start fall ploughing. We'd get back at the enemy; we'd destroy its food supply.

So Helen travelled with the "Boys" over the entire farm. No gates or fences stopped them. Alfred heard of a horse that sounded like a good buy, so he walked three miles cross-country to look it over, buy and lead it home accompanied by a colt we named Nip. Nip was independent; didn't give anyone a chance to like him. Our two cows and Helen pastured the farm with Nip. When Alfred was away working on neighbouring farms I tried to have the cows in for milking before he came home. A simple task and pleasant, to walk through the pasture, swatting the tops of mullein stocks, scanning the distant fields for a glimpse of Alfred to signal to with outflung arms.

As Helen's time drew near, we kept watch on her. Every night, if Alfred had been working away from home he would search her out, watch her habits, and assure himself she was all right perhaps for another day.

One evening she could not be found. A heavy fog, extreme for our district, was descending rapidly, so thick we had to wear raincoats.

"I've got to find her. She's due, and they often go off alone when they are about to freshen."

So we started out together until we realized darkness was falling fast; then Alfred went one way and I another, to meet. "No luck, no sign of her."

Again we started, soaked now and cold, our raincoats flopping on our fog-sodden overalls. My teeth chattered with the misery in my bones.

"I hope she appreciates what we are going through for her," I thought, trudging on, peering into fence corners and thickets. At last a call from Alfred. He'd found her in a spot he'd passed before. Together we herded her into the dry warmth of the stable, and by lantern light Alfred watched her calf born. This pretty little heifer with the wide beautiful eyes we decided to call Jeannie, after Mother.

Perhaps they are supposed to, I don't know, but animals will eat the afterbirth. Alfred tries to be there to get rid of it before they can, but Helen managed to get some and choked so badly that only quick action saved her. Alfred put his hand down her throat and pulled the membrane out; gratitude shone in Helen's eyes. She saw Alfred then, and knew him as her hero.

I missed all this, getting supper, but had my sequel to the story a year later. Is it elephants who never forget? Well, neither do cows. Jeannie was such a pretty little calf, but she did not do well. We couldn't figure it out. She nursed well, but was just not thrifty.

"It's malnutrition," Alfred said, and Jeannie died of it.

The vegetable garden that showed such promise, grew beautifully for a few inches, then stopped. We looked at it and said nothing. Dad looked at it and shook his head. Alfred looked at it and worried himself sick. The corn, peas and beans did not do well. We stopped expecting much from the potatoes. The "cash crop" became a pipe dream.

And we went doggedly on. The farm was ours, the life our choice, the work what we wanted to do. No man to call master, but the earth to become our mistress; to learn her vagaries, her complex nature, her need, greater than our own, and her gratitude. A mistress capable of unknown wonders, variable, yet insistent, in whose close association we were to find the greatest happiness in our exciting lives.

Alfred bought a walking plough and a set of disc harrows. This was the extent of his new equipment purchasing. In the early fall we watched the local paper for farm sales. Fully conscious of the extent to which the farm had been depleted of its natural fertility, Alfred with an oblivious, encouraging wife, went on spending our meagre store of capital judiciously and well. His tall figure, wearing with great poise and dignity the Indian sweater he liked so well, stood out in groups of sombre-clad farmers at the sales. Bidding cautiously, he was never caught with auction fever. If he was seen at a sale, it was because he wanted something listed; if it went beyond the price he judged fair he let it go. I've always marvelled at his ability to wait, when the article desired was something special and needed badly.

He had to borrow a car to attend one sale twelve miles distant. It was a profitable trip. Here he acquired a mowing machine, two years old and newly painted, for $53; a fourteen foot dump rake for $10; bobsleds, $20; hay fork and rope, $6; and as piece de resistance, a luxury—a rubber-tired wagon with hay rack for $80. (This was the first of its kind in our district.)

Alfred would never be able to do all our ploughing. Even if he had the time, his feet couldn't take it. All this year the incisions on his heels were open and draining. It worried me constantly. An old army veteran in town suggested he apply again to the V.L.A. people, which he did. This time there was no waiting; definitely and promptly the application was turned down, on the grounds that we were a poor risk on a run-out farm. The disappointment was great, but not a surprise. Looking at it from the standpoint of the V.L.A., Alfred said he'd turn the application down himself. But that was scant comfort, knowing how great the work of building up the fertility would be, with our capital. It meant a long period of years and good markets.

Reading the signs in the garden and among the livestock is a sobering thing. Even then, one is prone to wishful thinking. This was impressed on us, as we watched our first crop grow and mature, unable to do anything further to improve the soil. It was like a hungry monster calling for food and more food; we were helpless humble folk, with so little to give.

Now to the business of land, the fall ploughing. We found the Neilson Brothers in Fergus, who do custom ploughing at set prices for sod or stubble. Figuring what field to cultivate and how much we could afford to have done, it was arranged that they do the work for us. A jolly pair of brothers brought their cheerfulness and happy-go-lucky natures into our kitchen for uproarious meals, full of friendly jokes about people and farms to make us feel there were millions like us with the same problems. In order to get on to their next job one of the boys worked all night, and I got up earlier than usual to make him a good breakfast. I'll never get over feeling sorry for anyone who has to stay up all night to work. My night duty days when nursing are remembered torment. The less work I had to do the harder it was to stay awake. The harder I worked, the sicker the patient.

"Please, God, may I never do night duty again," I prayed. But I did, with pigs!

We didn't have any hay or straw to start the winter with. Alfred had to buy it from neighbouring farmers who had more than they needed for their stock.

We had bought a cream separator, secondhand, from a farmer, who was replacing it with an electric one. What luxury! The old floor in the kitchen, one day to be replaced, could not be damaged more, so Alfred bolted the separator to the floor near the window. Morning and night the hum of the separator was music to our ears; as we watched the stream of cream flowing into a clean white bowl, the milk to a pail for the pigs. With the lamps lit, the kettle boiling, something savory simmering on the stove and the separator humming, the old kitchen held warmth and industry. Contentment filled our hearts. With all these milk things to look after, why do all this work for so few cows, and plenty of room in the barn to stable more?

Alfred fancied a dairy herd. That way he could get a steady income. So he borrowed money to pay half the cost of seven Holstein cows and four heifers, guaranteed to freshen in three months. A creamery, seeking business promised Alfred a milk contract. This was wonderful. We bought a milking machine, partly because of the increased number of cows to milk; we felt that with a milk contract, we could afford one. Chiefly for a reason I knew nothing about, Alfred insisted I was not to learn to milk, and I was willing enough not to. He didn't tell me that after milking three or four cows, his right arm would ache and go numb due to injury overseas. I'm so glad I always encouraged him to purchase equipment that made work easier. What hurt me most to watch that winter was the patient way he worked at cleaning stables with an old broken down wheelbarrow. He replaced it with one he bought for the parts only, a good wheel and iron brackets, for fifty cents. The job was still a hard one; as he had also suffered an injury to his back, the bending and lifting crippled him always. I'd look at the litter carrier track on other farms we passed, and urge him to put one in our barn. It took five years of urging.

A second-hand hay-loader completed our equipment for that year. We were ready now for haying the following year. Again, we felt good with more stock in the barn than we expected to have our first winter, and equipment to get started with. Barney was a beautiful big black gelding. He would prance to work in the morning and prance home at night. Peggy would tire keeping up to him and let him do the lion's share of pulling. However, they were friends and Barney didn't mind.

Not long after the living-room was finished, Alfred went to work on a long-dreamed of project, a fire-place. My brother Perry is a contractor and bricklayer and the two men planned a large brick fire-place and proceeded to break a hole through the wall to build it. Lime was hard to get at this time, but they thought they had enough. The only window in the cellar had to be closed up, and the two amateur stone masons set to work. It soon developed that Alfred was doing the stone work and Perry the brick, but before they had gone very far, the lime ran out and there was no more to be had. It left a nice gap for any little animal that might care to come in the house, even the dog, a big shaggy mongrel that never outlived his puppy tricks. I left a little blue felt hat on the chesterfield one day, and he chewed it up. It was the hat I'd worn when Alfred and I met. The dog, long since dead, has never been forgiven by Alfred.

It was getting on in the fall and the living-room with its hole in the wall, was becoming uninhabitable. One afternoon the former owner came to call. She sat on a straight-backed chair facing the hole, and her expression hinted that she wished she had never sold the place to such a wanton people.

"Why, there are no blinds on the windows!" she remarked, and we said, "If anyone wants to come this far to peek in our windows, and lets us know, we will give them a show."

She shook her head sorrowfully and was gone.

For a few more weeks we had to sit in the kitchen or go to bed. Shopping for a stove to set up in the living-room sounds such a simple task if you have the money to pay for it. We found it very difficult. Some sort of price war kept the warehouses full, and the merchants had nothing to sell. We intended having a nice looking stove for the living-room, a new one. Came

November, and the winds were cold and damp. Not far out of Elora there was a sale of household goods, with two Quebec heaters listed. I went with a neighbour. The smaller of the two stoves looked in best repair, newer and no rust spots. The bidding between myself and a slight young woman was lively. She was determined to have that stove. I looked at her several times. She looked cold; no stockings, and her blue hands were clasping and unclasping nervously. I let it go for $8. Now I really examined the second one, twice the size of the other, dirty, rusty, ugly as sin. A man watching me commented, "About three dollars worth of repairs will make it look like new." So I bid on the stove and got it, complete with a pan full of ashes, for three dollars!

Alfred emptied the ashes, spent thirty cents on repairs, polished it up and put it up in the living-room on a nice shiny stand. It doesn't matter how ugly a stove is when there is a fire burning in it to give warmth. There is a beauty—warm, close and comforting—no indirect heating can give. Or am I sentimental? I don't like cleaning out ashes either.

Our harvest was in for this year; potatoes enough for our own use. How many bags had we hoped to sell? Corn practically destroyed by the "Boys," sparse anyway, gave us a taste of how delicious our own home canned corn could be. We canned: 69 cans of corn, 14 cans of peas, 14 cans of beans, 14 cans of tomatoes, 36 cans of apple sauce (without sugar), 6 cans of green gages, 46 jars of wild raspberry jam and 16 jars of wild strawberry jam.

The birds beat me to the red currants. I'd be smarter next year. The apple sauce was made from wind falls, tubs of them picked daily, little railroad wormy apples. I literally crawled around each apple getting the bit of unspoiled pulp for my sauce that each one had. It was fruit for the winter, and that first summer I thought I had all the time in the world to do anything.

Doing these homey things increased my sense of security, while growing accustomed to a new way of life. Being busy, going to bed tired each night, increased my feeling of usefulness and importance. There was no time for discontent.

News travels quickly via the grapevine in the country, and no doubt our characteristics were known in advance, for we were barely established in the deserted house before it was prophesied that we would last two years. We had come as strangers to a community where farms had continued in one family for several generations. Our farm was known to be run out. This was during a period when farm produce commanded a high price. Everyone was busily engaged in taking everything from the soil that it could give. They knew we couldn't get much. Our plight would be bad, but we would soon be gone. They were polite and indifferent. We went to church and felt like Exhibit A, stared at, smiled at when a gaze was caught unawares, but we remained outsiders. Alfred tried to discuss farm practices with them, but all were non-committal. He soon found that he would learn nothing from them, and never asked advice or assistance. We tried to take an active part in a Farm Forum group, but it died a natural death for lack of interest. However, we continued always to be on friendly speaking terms with our neighbours.

Top: Field left bare over winter without benefit of cover crop or sod bears witness to sheet and soil erosion and lack of organic matter.

Bottom: Field, half sown in fall rye and half left bare, showing prevention of erosion by cover crop.

—Courtesy Dept. of Public Relations, O.A.C., Guelph.

Top: Showing proper land usage. Field too difficult to harvest by machinery is harvested without difficulty by grazing cattle on it.

Bottom: Soil improvement pays off. Formerly barren knoll, now producing excellent crop of grass and legumes, pastured herd of Hereford shorthorn beef cattle.

CHAPTER 5

This was like a dream world I was living in. To be a homemaker had always been my chief ambition; something I never hesitated to admit to myself in all the years I had followed a profession. That it had come true was almost impossible to believe. However, wanting this way of life didn't make me the world's best home-maker. Alfred tells me now he often thought he'd got a lemon when it came to cooking. That first summer the meals were terrible. They were a bugbear to me too. I was too cautious in my spending and too inexperienced both in cooking and managing a wood or coal fire. Alfred was patient. He had enough to worry about. My optimism never faltered. A rosy vision of how things would look when we did such and such became so much a game with us, that the spot where the granary board cupboard stood was known as the place where we would put the electric stove. The sink would be in front of the window overlooking the lawn towards the crab-apple tree. Upstairs, one room we called the bathroom while all the time necessity took us to a little grey board house behind the back shed. Here one felt a false seclusion when, keeping the door open to contemplate the apple trees in bloom, a passing car would be heard and you'd be caught, locked quickly in its disagreeable darkness.

Alfred received a small pension now, and I was getting a few cents for eggs; the cream cheque too, was the beginning of an income. However, with mill feeds to buy for chickens, pigs and cattle, also hay and straw, the balance sheet was all in the red. This had to be changed, as quickly as possible. We were too anxious to get the business of farming under way to mark time till spring, when we'd sow our first crop. If we just broke even, buying everything as we had to, at least there would be the manure and the calves to start the spring with. I'd really have something to bring in from the pasture next summer.

The promised milk contract would bring us $1.50 more per cwt. for whole milk, and with our good-looking Holsteins in the stable, things looked bright. We named each beast after a friend or relation. It made working in the barn friendly, fostering an intimacy between us and the cattle, amusing and pleasant. Lily had overpowered Maggie, to become head of the herd, but her supremacy didn't last long. Bessie took over. Driving them in from the pasture, I felt very sorry for Lily, having to follow in second place. We had had her longer and our friendship was deeper. Bessie still had to prove herself, so I resented her taking the lead so soon.

As far as budgeting was concerned, we didn't. Initial expenditures had been made, and what remained deposited in a joint account, with a separate wedding-gift account in my name, where we planned to put all the profits from poultry, with which we would do special things. Looking over our bank balance, Alfred said:

"Well, there it is. Spend it as you like. If we can't add to it, that's our hard luck."

So, whether we could afford anything or not, if we felt that we had to have it, we did. Things like the new floor and linoleum in the kitchen that winter; we couldn't afford it, but life without it was going to be dashed uncomfortable. In December we bought the milking machine. We couldn't afford it, but neither could Alfred afford to do without it. He soon learned that work had to be as light as possible if it was to be done with efficiency. So these things we bought or planned for, with no compunction about their advisability with our capital.

I bought food with care. My greatest problem was avoiding spoilage in summer or winter, although it kept better in winter. None of the cows or heifers we bought that fall, due to freshen in a specified time, did so. In fact several were a long way off the date stated. This was very aggravating, but the cattle were nice, so we kept our grievance to ourselves, wiser for another time.

For that first Christmas in our own home, I went into town with a neighbour to purchase extras, having invited my parents, a sister and two elderly aunts for the day. The five-and-ten-cent store absorbed all my attention. Tinsel to catch the lamplight had to be bought, since the tree could not be decorated with lights. For a game we could all play, I chose a double

feature, Chinese checkers and an ordinary checker board combined.

Christmas week arrived, and Alfred worked in the kitchen
with me, making mincemeat, cakes, plum pudding and Christmas candies. The illustrations in every magazine at that time of
year looked so simple and we would try anything once. We
dipped chocolates and made coloured mints. Then we made a
table ornament, using half a birch log, with four holes for candles.

We decorated the log with whipped wax, and coloured
little wax balls, making red berries. This simulated snow, and
with mica sparkling over it, and bits of red and green with little
pine cones here and there, it made a truly lovely decoration.

Christmas Eve arrived, and Alfred set a fire in the fireplace
for the first time. The decorated tree sparkled in the firelight.
The dinner table was set at one side, with its snowy cloth,
crackers and lovely, candle-lit ornament. We needed no alco-
holic beverage to celebrate. We were intoxicated with our own
joy and love. We had peace on earth, and soon it would be
Christmas Day in the morning.

Our local clergyman called and took us all to early service
and back home again. Then came the excitement of cooking the
first Christmas dinner. I was naturally anxious to impress the
family with my prowess. After it was over, Dad came to me in
the kitchen and said:

"It's the best Christmas dinner I've ever had, Margaret.
You're doing fine."

"Thanks, Dad," I murmured, filled with emotion and contentment.

After the New Year celebrations were over, we tackled the
kitchen, stripping the walls of nine layers of paper, just as hard
to get off as the living-room paper had been. I don't know now
how we managed, in the confusion of laying a new floor and
putting down linoleum in the kitchen; Alfred spending hours
daily plastering cracks, and finally painting the kitchen a nice
ivory. I did a lot of the cooking in the living-room on the
Quebec stove that gave us great comfort.

Oh, we were a busy pair that first winter. Alfred built cupboards on either side of the south kitchen window, where the
sink would be one day. I would need the cupboards when we

had to take the granary boards back to the barn, come harvest time. He did not put doors on them for two very good reasons, of which I approved. I would have to keep them tidier without doors to shut on disorder; and then my Old Willow dishes, nicely arranged, gave a warm and friendly atmosphere.

When Alfred's appointment for his yearly physical examination at Westminster Hospital arrived, Dad offered to come out and stay with me.

It was the year of the big snow, and there was warning of uncertain weather at that time. Our neighbour left his car on the main road at another farm. We would go across the field by sleigh or cutter, stable the horses in the farmer's barn and take the car to town from there. By this means, Alfred brought Dad from Fergus. The roads were open then. We called the local taxi, which was also the mail carrier from the train to post office, run by a woman. She was to pick Alfred up at the farm on the main road the following afternoon. By morning, no one could possibly get through. Alfred notified her to this effect. Unless the snow plough went through first. It didn't. We took Alfred across and down the highway a short distance, till it became unwise to go further. From there he walked an approximate five miles, on snow banks that reached and towered over the telephone lines. There was not even a foot path to follow on the road, and snow kept falling.

When he reached the station, the train was five hours late. Nothing to do but sit on the hard benches and wait. That waiting room became a familiar place, with its big pot-bellied stove in the centre, seats all round the walls, and a scattering of dejected travellers restlessly uncomfortable on them. Alfred contemplated the picture of an ocean liner for some time, living again the trip he had made in this same ship in 1939 with the first convoy to England of Canadian troops. Now the aftermath found him in this miserable position, footsore, and because of it having to go to London for a checkup. And he knew that he was lucky.

No one talked much till a clergyman came in and, finding an audience of half a dozen, proceeded to take the floor. He attracted little interest until he started in on the atrocious gall of a farmer who had expected the taxi to go into the country for him on a day like this. The very idea of asking this of anyone, let alone a woman, was beyond words.

Alfred eyed him with smouldering anger at such garbling of a normal call for a taxi.

"I am that farmer. When I called for the taxi she could have driven to my door. No one expected her to go into the country today. I walked in."

No one in the room mentioned weather again. They couldn't best Alfred's feat of walking five miles, and I wonder what they really would have thought had they known the condition of his feet.

I was so relieved when he called me from the station to say that he had arrived, but sorry he had to wait five hours for the train in that dismal place.

At home, I didn't dare think of what the storm could mean, isolated now as we were. Dad would be lost without a daily paper or his walk to town.

It was four a.m. when Alfred finally reached London that night, and he had to stay over a second night.

I painted the medicine chest for our bathroom corner in the kitchen; fussed with the meals, and tried not to let Dad see how worried about everything I really was. With Alfred away, the farm lost its warmth. The work became drudgery. Loneliness overwhelmed me, responsibility became a great weight that tired and frightened me.

When Alfred got back, following the snow plough's last trip for two weeks or more, responsibility rolled off me like water. We got Dad home again. We had piles of accumulated papers and mail to read, and we had each other.

Like squirrels, we were well stocked for winter. Salt, sugar, flour, tea, coffee, yeast. Let the wind blow; let it snow! We loved our little world and the beauty of the snow-covered hills and valleys all around. Depending entirely on each other and the work we were doing together, outside interests were of little consequence. We welcomed our isolation and thoroughly enjoyed it. No electricity cut-off or failure due to the storm affected us. Bins full of coal and plenty of wood, large cans of coal oil for the lamps and lanterns, kept us secure and self-sustaining. There were only the regular trips to the barn to care for the stock to disturb us. Once there, feeding the placid cows, gathering eggs, and feeding busy industrious chickens, feeding the gluttonous pigs, squealing at their trough; little pigs, eyes turned up watchful and waiting. Horses whinnying and stamping back and forth, and the barn odours, helped one forget the storm outside, for it is warm in the stable and peaceful.

The heavy snow continued till the villages were cleared out of their stock of bread and yeast. No one could buy bread, so I made extra for our neighbour, feeling justly proud. A town girl, spending her first winter on the farm, able to come to the rescue of real farm folk, who had been born and brought up in the country 1

Eventually the storm passed and roads were opened up to us. It was like going through a tunnel, the banks were so high. They had to get a bulldozer to open our side road. Then it rained and froze, turning the world around us into a fairy land of glittering crystal; everything danced and sparkled in the sunlight. Each little breeze started up an orchestra of tinkling sounds.

Across this fairy scene floundered five grade cows Alfred had bought from a local dealer to augment our milk supply when other cows went dry. The truck was unable to get.beyond the brow of the hill at the eastern tip of our farm, so the poor beasts had to struggle through a twelve acre field quite deep with snow, now covered with a thick ice-like crust. Sometimes the crust was strong enough to hold them up, but more often than not they broke through with one or two feet.

I felt desperately sorry for the poor beasts being urged gently on by Alfred and the dealer and anxious to see them safe in the stable. They were so patient, so resigned under duress. It was hard to believe each one would have a character all its own, and that we would soon recognize it.'

We were promised a milk contract, and enough was being taken as consumer milk to encourage us in pursuing a dairy programme. We had bought a milking machine. This and the washing machine gave us a real lift. But, to help take the drudgery out of farming, there was no reason why we could not enjoy that exquisite luxury of breakfast in bed. Every Sunday we took turns. Alfred did all the chores and milking one day, and I the next. I can't describe the feeling of importance or how capable

I felt the morning I slipped quickly out of bed and, gathering up the milk pail and milker, crunched through the snow to the barn. I changed the milker from one cow to the next, methodically going down the line, emptying the pail through a strainer into the huge cans anchored in the water trough for quick cooling. Back at the house again, Alfred, roused by the odour of coffee and bacon tickling his nostrils would come down and I'd probably go back to bed again. It was equally as nice the morning Alfred brought breakfast up to me. We knew how to relax whenever we could.

A mild spell in February brought promise of spring. The roads were rivers of slush and bare patches appeared in the fields.

I would go to the barn with Alfred after supper, to bed and water the stock. Alfred gave them their hay when he milked before supper and it was light, throwing the hay down from the barn floor. Single file, the flickery circle of light from the lantern picking out the almost blown-in footprints of earlier trips to the barn, our shoulders hunched, heads down, silently we would hurry through the storm to the welcome warmth of the stable.

First he would water the animals, carry bucketful after bucketful to a trough he had made in front of the mangers, filling it and keeping it full till the cows stopped drinking, knowing then that there would be plenty for their wants till morning. Then he'd lead the horses to the trough; they looked tremendous in the low run-in shed. And next the bedding; not too plentiful, it was not wasted, yet the animals were kept clean and dry.

And now a last look down the feed alleys to see it there might be a little to fork into the mangers. Ah, yes, long tongues curled out and licked it in. There was enough, but we would have liked to give them more. When the roads were passable again, Alfred would shop round for more hay. I was full of questions and Alfred patient and detailed with his answers. We liked doing things together. I never tired listening to pleasant sounds of the animals, a horse pawing its stall or whinnying, the creak of neck chains and cattle eating or drinking. The colour, the warm dark brown shadows softening the grey stone wall and hand hewn beams and posts; the light of the lantern catching a bit of golden straw; it all gave serene beauty to the humble picture. Something enduring and changeless, filling me with peace and well-being and thoughts of God.

I once heard a clergyman state, "The unknown God is greater than the revealed God." Here in the stable I feel He is revealing Himself as I watch, with humility and wonder, a baby calf being born and see its mother's wide pain-filled eyes, as in complete silence she submits to the order of life, her body restless and tormented. Then, at the moment of its birth her eyes change to great pools of tenderness, and with a quiet lowing, she calls her baby to her. The little thing struggles to its wobbly feet, all wet and warm and steaming and, finding its mother's head with unerring skill, settles down to rest and be bathed until it is dry by an ever watchful mother, all pain forgotten, content to serve and give all that she has to this her offspring. I can understand now why the Christian story begins in a stable, where the magnificence of Nature in the humblest of surrounding, with perfect simplicity, enacts the miracle of birth.

"Thank you for this life," I whisper, clasping Alfred's hand, and turning back through the pump-house where we get a pail of water for the house, we go up the orchard to our home.

There was no ending to our talk of plans for the first crop year. With the milk contract still promised but not executed, we had to arrange something to cool the milk rapidly in summer. With no electricity to service milk coolers, the next best thing was ice. Alfred arranged to buy eighty-five bags of sawdust at a mill in Alma, and went one day to start hauling it. Our side road was not open right through to the highway, neither was the cross road. So he had to take a very long route round the Goose Neck, a winding road up a hill several miles out of our way. Trying to bring an extra large load, last thing at night, the hill was too much for the horses, not sharp shod, so half of it was dumped on the side of the road. After chores and supper were over, we bundled up warm and set off to get the balance of the load. The moon was full, the air sharp, with frost. Warm and happy, we enjoyed this drive through the stillness, feeling a part of it and the beauty of the night. The ice, Alfred cut on the stream that bordered our property. It was a lot of work done willingly to produce a good product. The seed catalogues were good for many hours of vivid imagining minus the manual labour. Alfred gave serious attention to the grass seed he would buy for eleven acres; all we could afford to seed down the first year. Seed grain purchased from a neighbour took the last of our $1,400 for stock and equipment.

Now I started keeping books in earnest. Everything had been going out. Small as it was, we already had some income from our investment, and it had to be put to the best possible advantage. To do this, we had to keep an accurate account of costs for each branch of our enterprise; namely, pigs, chickens and dairy. Anything we could do as a side line to augment this income would be all to the good.

The maple trees were tapped and we made four gallons of syrup. I promptly gave three away in over-exuberance, which put that enterprise on the wrong side of the ledger for this year anyway. Alfred read continuously, and discussed with me articles and pamphlets on agriculture. This was gaining a healthy respect from me, who had thought all you had to do was plant a seed, water it, and it would produce abundantly. That the soil was anything other than dirt under my feet, which clung to them because of the law of gravitation, was new to me.

Helen's calf, Jeannie, died after a month or so, and Alfred was sure it was malnutrition. Then an apparently healthy calf born during the winter died after a few days of life. We were sure the soil was the villain. It deceived us. It was there; it looked like any other soil; but it could not produce. Our garden had been proof that our livestock, deficient in necessary minerals and trace elements, could not be thrifty and profitable. A few losses would soon eat up our profits. It was a sobering thought to start the spring work with. Alfred determined to get all the information he could from every source. All that we had went into the seed and fertilizer (the first the farm had ever known). Not knowing what it really needed, we gave all we could afford. The neighbourhood didn't think we had much of a chance to survive, we learned later.

CHAPTER 6

With more time to think of myself now, I decided I should have a permanent. After all, one must keep up one's appearance. I made an appointment. Alfred was to drive me over on the sleigh to the Alma station, where I'd take the train to Fergus. In the evening he would come in the borrowed car for a game of bridge with Mother and Dad and bring his beautified wife home again.

All very simple, it seemed, until we found that the snow plough had gone only a hundred feet down the side road. We floundered on. The horses, up to their bellies in snow, hampered by harness and hitched to a sleigh, were frantic. And then the reach broke. Worse still, Alfred's mitts had holes in them. I should have been at home mending or knitting him more. My nylons, wet with snow, were freezing my legs. The wind was turning my hat askew. I looked a poor, unsuitably dressed excuse for a farmer's wife. Alfred's silence as he unhitched the horses to right the sleigh made me feel worse. He begged me to cut across the fields to the station. I wouldn't go. Silence held us as we listened helplessly to the train whistle and watched its billowing smoke trail through the sky towards Fergus. Why we went on I don't really know; perhaps because there was a telephone in the station and I might locate a ride. I did, with our local auctioneer. Late for the appointment, but she took me. The game of bridge, and wavy hair to soften my face, melted the ice. I vowed never again to have my hair done in town, and have kept that vow. Even though I half drown myself with solutions and rinsing, the hair is curled at home.

It was luxurious, this being alone, spending so much of our day together, through the month of February and on into March. The grass seed Alfred ordered for eleven acres was stored safely, with a mouse trap set beside it, behind the living-room door. We talked and talked over plans to make money, so that we could buy better and more equipment, and of course eventually modernize the house.

It was cold upstairs every time a north wind blew, we had a good sized snowdrift just inside our bedroom door where the floor had sunk away from the wainscoting. It took the clothes I hung in the ghost walk a week to dry. Apart from the "bathroom," which was warm, the upper floor was so cold as winter progressed that I cleaned only when compelled to by my conscience or the dust I could not avoid seeing.

Alfred had to buy more hay. I watched in terror as the wagon negotiating icy roads came down our hill and turned in at the lane. I wished fervently for spring when the cattle would get out to pasture.

We had four little calves. I'd feed them two at a time. It was always a contest. Would they spill half the milk down my rubber boot in their enthusiasm to get at it, or would I be able to keep perfect balance and guide the pail so the bunting head always went straight in. I'd change my theory of how I should approach the calves and how the pails should be held every time I fed them. The calves were good for a lot of laughs and exasperation.

Among the pullets were three roosters, beautiful proud birds strutting nobly among the hens. I had three steps to go up when entering the chicken house and another inside it. This gave Mr. Rooster a superior position, and he grew quite cocky, starting with little attacks on my legs, till finally he began flying at me, and my nervous awareness turned to fear. Alfred laughed at me being afraid of a rooster, but suggested I take a stick. This gave me courage and I was more offensive; thus the battle began. I was going to get that rooster and it was equally determined to get me. As I had a pail of feed or water or a basket of eggs in one hand, the more agile rooster generally had the advantage, but I did get in a few swats, enough to let him know I meant business. Perhaps he knew we had killed and eaten the other two, and didn't intend meeting the same fate.

One day Alfred was in the chicken house and rooster made a mistake. He flew at him. Picking up a stick Alfred struck him on the head, laying him flat and he thought dead. But Mr. Rooster revived, to stagger to his feet, take a few steps, lose his balance, go down, up again and with flapping wings try to keep on his feet. All his proud dignity was gone and he looked so pathetic. Much as I disliked him for his behaviour towards me, I could not see this proud bird so degraded before all his harem. "Please kill him. I can't bear to see him so disgraced." So we had him for Sunday dinner.

Unable to watch me rubbing clothes on a washboard, Alfred went against principle and bought on time a washing machine with a gasoline engine, pledging his pension cheque till it was paid for. I couldn't remonstrate with a man who did such thoughtful things for me, but he should have kept that money for farm equipment. Besides, it was wonderful to have it and maybe the profits from the chickens would pay for it eventually.

The Neilson Brothers came back to cultivate the forty acres they had ploughed in the fall, and Alfred and I cleared a large space in the barn floor to treat the seed grain. A man came in to arrange to haul sand from the gravel pit. He told Alfred we would make enough out of it to pay our taxes anyway, which was nice, and they made a deal satisfactory to both.

With a borrowed seeder, Peggy and Barney were eager to be off. I had to stand at their heads while Alfred hitched. I stood by the corner of the barn watching Alfred's long legs striding behind the seeder. He watched so closely as he went up and down the field sowing our hope for a bounteous harvest. No one would know, watching him, that it was all he could do to keep going. Determination and will power kept him going till the job was finished, and we would wait and watch the first crop break through the soil, grow and mature.

This farm had not been seeded down to grasses and legumes for a possible ten years previously, and hay had been sold off it. Alfred remembered also the short pasture the cattle had our first summer. He felt he must have something our cattle could use for pasture as the season advanced, so he planted strips of fodder corn, sorghum and millet. Alfred was an experimenter, and this his first experimental plot. He wanted to know how much forage each would produce.

One night in August after a heavy rain, the cattle had broken through the fence and were where they should not be. Sometimes I wondered if it was a good idea to go out for the evening. If we had been in bed we'd never have known it till morning. But knowing, there was just one thing to do; get them back where they belonged. So down through the swampy section of Alfred's test plot we ran through the dark, blindly chasing the sound of cattle. Corn, sorghum and millet, wet and thick, slapped us mercilessly as we tried to break through it. I could always give up farming very easily at moments like this, but it would soon be forgotten when the sun came up in the morning, and I knew I had been helpful.

The fences were our responsibility now, and without exception all the bad ones were ours. It took all the time and more that Alfred had for odd jobs before haying. Mid-morning generally found Alfred somewhere near the house, and I would take two cups, all that was left usually, of coffee out to sit in a fence corner, or on anything handy out of the wind. A pause in the midst of our perplexities, to talk, sip coffee and be together in the sun. It gave me renewed vigour, reducing my little problems to inconsequence. Alfred too felt better in knowing I was always near with encouragement to counteract his doubts.

In the afternoon, a sandwich and a piece of cake went with the coffee. We had a happy time watching the grain shoots turn the brown earth to green. Every Sunday we walked around the farm. It wasn't very encouraging. The grain was a poor colour. Later it stopped growing and matured too early. The knolls were barely covered, and here the grain dried up.

"It's a terrible crop."

Alfred was depressed. We had put everything we had in this farm and it looked as if it could never produce anything, even the barest living. I was too stupid, fortunately, to appreciate the seriousness of all the signs Alfred noted on our Sunday walks. Blissfully ignorant and equally happy, reassuring him always, doing my very best to help in every way, I must have helped him stick with it then.

We borrowed a spraying apparatus, and with me at the pump one horse pulled the barrel of spray with its pump on a little sleigh, similar to the one Alfred had made on our honeymoon, through the orchard. We had to get the best possible production from everything we had. The apples netted us twenty-one dollars. We had corn for canning planted too.

To save Alfred's feet as much as possible, I always went for the cows in the morning and at night. They were pasturing below the cedars and in the back field. Alfred would stand at the barn door and watch me swinging down the lane and up the hill. Here I always turned to fling wide my arms in greeting and he would do the same. Never losing consciousness of one another has made the going easier. By the time I reached the top of the hill, always hurrying in the morning, I'd be breathless. The pause for greeting gave me my second wind. Depending on where the cows were, we'd come back either the way I had gone, or around the cedars, which was longer, so we had to hurry a bit.

Alfred did a lot of thinking, and fortunately for me he did it out loud. We would talk on into the night; plans, possibilities. I felt awfully important having him discuss problems with me, even though I knew nothing about them. My confidence and encouragement were all he needed. That was all I had to give and I gave it whole-heartedly, my contribution to the business.

With all the neighbours busy on their own farms, we were very much on our own. Not until harvesting, when Alfred worked in with four others, did he have opportunity to discuss crops, soils, ways and means with people who knew what he was talking about, whether they had anything to contribute or not.

We depended, our first crop year, on the grasses and weeds, natural to our soil that had grown there for years without being reseeded, for our hay crop. A sad crop it was too; just like the hay loader Alfred bought with some cattle, which broke down never to go again before we had got properly started. Our best bit of hay was cut too, and just about ready to bring in. We would have to wait till a neighbour finished his before we could use his loader. So it rained, but just before the sudden storm broke, we rushed out, swirling the windrows into cocks in order that as little as possible would be spoiled by getting wet. The storm broke with fury, lightning and thunder, wind and rain. Alfred kept right on cocking hay, so terrified, I kept right on too. We were breathless when it was done and back in the house, we stood at the window and watched the rain come down. A blessing to the thirsty grain, and ruin to cut hay.

"What we have must go in, in the best possible condition, if we want to make the difference between profit and loss this year. The grain needs this rain badly."

So we settled down to an unexpected afternoon in the house, a precious respite in a busy season.

Later, Alfred threw this saved hay on the wagon, with me building the load. From then on I drove the horses while Alfred built the loads, using our neighbours' hay loader. Leading the horse on the hay fork I did not like, ever. It's simple enough, but I could manage to make turning complicated and get under the horses feet all too frequently. We learned what our average quota per day was that summer, and the grass thereafter was cut accordingly, so none would be left out longer than necessary. Not trying to do more than we could, and still be on speaking terms, was a wise thing to do, which we practised in every operation, barring emergencies.

Violent storms were frequent that summer. The worst blew up suddenly the morning Alfred took the borrowed binder back to its owner, and I didn't know till he got home again if he got there before it broke or not. So terrified, sure my last moment was at hand and not caring much, for Alfred must have been caught also, my vivid imagination really carried me into the depths that day. I poured myself a cup of coffee, took it to the chesterfield and lay down, thinking if this is to be it I might just as well be comfortable. A neighbouring barn was struck and burned to the ground. I could have seen it from a window of the living-room but lay unaware of it, too terrified to move until the storm was over, and Alfred phoned that he was safe.

Our hay crop averaged a half ton to the acre of poor hay, though well saved from rain damage. Alfred arranged to buy the hay from a three-acre piece owned by a neighbour who had more than he needed. This, fortunately, was cut and raked for us. All we had to do was load it and bring it home. I continued to drive the horses down the road, feeling very proud and happy, till I was making the turn at the gate with my heart in my mouth, certain I'd tip the load. I didn't. So we continued to bring forage to the farm, making up a little for the years it had been sold off the land.

On rainy days, I'd clean the house enough to keep my self-respect, and bake. Alfred would help me with the dishes and getting quick meals on the days we worked together in the field. First things came first, which was the field work and livestock.

After that we did what we could in the house. Between haying and harvest, the wild raspberries were ripe in the bush. I picked every day, with Alfred helping once in a while, and made lots of good raspberry jam. Like squirrels, we were getting ready for winter again. I had to make a hurried trip to town with a part from the mowing machine to be fixed at the blacksmith's. Alfred hitched Snow White, a horse he bought for twenty-one dollars at a neighbour's sale because he knew how well he performed the previous year when Alfred worked there at harvest time. I named the horse Snow White for no other reason than that he was white. He weighed one ton. It was my first trip to town alone by horse and buggy and I quite enjoyed it. Very proud and pleased with myself I drove up to the blacksmith shop. The startled owner happened to be near the door and came out. "How do you like Snow White?" I asked.

He laughed and forgot his habit of being too busy to do a quick repair. I left the part, tied the horse in the church shed, and "did the town" while I waited. It was the only excursion of its kind I ever had, and I am so glad there was that one. Driving along country roads behind a horse, you see and feel the beauty around you more intensely than in a car, with a top over your head and the slowest speed still too fast.

We weren't too happy about the marketing of our milk. The milk contract did not materialize, and too much of the milk was taken for manufacturers at $1.50 per cwt. less than the other. Having it at the gate before seven, cooled and ready for collection, became too much of a chore for what we made out of it. One day in Elmira with a little surplus money to put to good advantage, we bought an engine; three horsepower, water-cooled. Alfred rigged up a line shaft for the milker, pump jack and separator. We were mechanized. No more pumping to fill the trough for the stock or turning the separator by hand. And the milker. One experience with its little engine going on the blink was quite enough for us. I learned to milk in a hurry that night.

Alfred had taken the engine to a machinist to fix and we had gone on into town with our borrowed car to do a number of important messages. Coming home about six, first we had trouble with the car, and it had to be left at a garage for repairs. The garageman drove us to collect our engine, and it wasn't ready. We had to go home to milk by hand fourteen cows! I milked three, working steadily without a break. Alfred did the other eleven in the same time, with time out for a smoke. Now we had the bigger engine, that nightmare would not be repeated, and a lot of hard work was taken out of our dairy pro- gramme. We shipped cream, and fed the skim milk to pigs.

Every Tuesday and Friday morning the dairy truck came in for cream and eggs, and once a week the driver brought the money for the previous week's produce. After he left, generally about 9 a.m., we would pull our chairs back to the table, pour out a cup of coffee, dump the money on the table, empty our purse, and count our cash. Then we'd plan what it had to do, till finally our money became known to us as "The Doings."

Not getting the milk contract was a very hard blow to take. We would have to just pull in our belts a little tighter.

CHAPTER 7

There was always a farmer with his team loading chop at the mill I passed as a child going to and from school. My fascination for horses had soon put us on friendly terms and generally I manoeuvred to drive the team to the corner. Remembering these happy days, driving our own team on the hay loader held no qualms for me till I was up there, perched on a cross piece of the front of the hay rack, with everything rattling as the wagon and hay rack lumbered along, empty, to the field. I had also driven the dump rake, and left a weaving windrow that would add to my difficulties now. Poor Alfred had enough troubles of his own keeping his balance building the load, with feet that only half belonged to him. There was no relaxation in this operation, attractive as it was to look at from a distance. The easy grace of Alfred forking hay into position on the load, as it was brought up by the rattling monster behind the wagon, was in reality a sight equal to the balancing act of a tight rope walker, with me, the driver, his balancing pole. I could never remember in my nervous excitement which meant "gee" and which "haw." Eyes all round our heads would have been of tremendous benefit. Fortunately, the horses were well trained, at least they knew enough to stop abruptly when told to, even if they couldn't read my mind when I called "Gee" and meant "Haw."

As the load grew, I dizzily ascended the front of the rack and finally teetered on top. Not daring to look down, I was yet compelled to by some magnetic force, perhaps the graceful rhythm of the broad hindquarters of the horses rising and falling with each step they took, accompanied by a gentle sound of harness creaking and trace chains clanking. The smell of warm horse flesh mingling with the pungent sweet perfume of new mown hay was intoxicating. The wagon would lurch to one side due to a wheel sinking in a hidden groundhog hole, and stark terror would seize me, looking back to make sure Alfred was safe and meeting smouldering anger in his eyes.

"Why can't you be more careful. Couldn't you see the groundhog hole?"

Finally the load is on, the loader detached, and we both want a brief respite, but I have no answer to:

"Of course you can drive them back to the barn. It's easy."

There would be no rest for Alfred at the barn, as he had to mow back as much as possible each time so I didn't fuss.

Of course, climbing practically over the horses' backs to go up and down each time I fixed the fork wasn't any relaxation, nor the tremendous effort it took to push the fork in as far as possible. Only after a dash to the house for a drink between loads and the pause while we sipped our drinks did we regain our sense of perspective.

Each load in was an accomplishment. Any little irritation or frayed temper was forgotten in sharing our satisfaction, and we didn't forget to tell each other, "I love you," and ride back to the field standing together, feet apart to brace ourselves and show how well balanced we were. Two kids, reassuring one another before our next attack on the job that must be done. One thing we learned; five loads a day were our limit. After that the tensions of the day left us so tired it would be dangerous to our home life to attempt more. Alfred cut what he estimated could be brought in in five loads, and only when the weather report promised rain or uncertain weather did we take in more, if it happened to be cut.

An unwritten law in our house is to be at the radio for the weather reports in the morning at noon and at night. We followed them implicitly, governing all the field work according to the predictions. This resulted in our hay being unspoiled by rain. Our nerves may have been frayed, but were never allowed to stretch to the breaking point.

Interferences in the daily routine kept us on our toes and active mentally as well as physically. It was a rare day that went according to plan. We started at break of day, when a faint pink blush came slowly over the grey blue mist of morning, the air cool and pungent with earthly, ripe harvest smells. It was like stepping into fairy land as I hurried past the barn, climbed the gate because it was too heavy to open, and hurried down the

66

lane into the cloudlike haze that lay in denser patches in the low spots. Each footstep left a dark green impression on the dew-misted grass. As the sun sent its first long slanting rays across the fields, a million diamonds sparkled on the grass. The morning symphony of bird songs filled the stillness, and I wished I didn't have to hurry so. As I approached, the cows would lift their heads and watch me for one long pondering moment, then, almost as if they had arranged the moves, wander leisurely to strategic spots, as far apart as possible, so that I would have to do a little more than rounding them up. Either it was a game, or they wanted one more choice morsel of dewy clover before the sun dried it.

"Can't you get them in any faster? I'll be late at the neighbour's." This was a neighbour with whom Alfred exchanged work.

"I did my best," wearily I'd reply. The spell is broken. Work without pleasure rears its ugly head, while the cows, all innocent and languid, let down their milk; nothing but tranquillity is registered there. I haven't time to be disagreeable. The fire has to be lit and, like as not, some kindling found to start it quickly. A stickler for being on time, Alfred must be away across the fields to the farm where the threshing is being done before eight o'clock.

When he is gone, the day looms up as long, long hours of emptiness and work, some hard and disagreeable, some as pleasant as I am in the mood to make it. If by chance we parted on a sour note, I'm miserable, and can't wait till he returns. It is a wretched day with the sun shining brightly and not a cloud in the sky. Perhaps I'll see him working in a near field, his blue clad figure standing out, slim and free against the golden grain and blue sky.

How often I tell myself, "He worries, and suffers far more than I am remotely aware of, and when he is quick to anger he is suffering the most." Then, with renewed determination, I try harder than ever to take the place of the expert help he needs, ever conscious of how willing my spirit is and how weak the flesh. "Dear God," I pray, "don't let me fail him, don't let me hold him back from anything he desires." At night, I go for the cows again, to have them all in for Alfred when he gets home. I walk over the same ground in such a different atmosphere from early morning. Now it is dry and warm, a seductive noisy silence compels me to drag my footsteps, loathe to leave the shelter of the cedars and the wilderness that is the pasture. The peace of the evening, with the deepening shadows cool and inviting and the gold of the grain ready for harvest giving in its richest hue, a false promise of abundance. All work should cease with this flaming exit of a golden day, to carry the tired farmer through a night of dreamless sleep, making him fresh for the morning. But no, off in the distance I hear the hum of a mower, the rattle of wagon wheels hauling in yet another load of grain to the threshers in the barn, men's voices and dogs barking. So, roused from my peaceful dream, I herd my wandering cows along the winding paths they follow to the barn. There are a lot of things to do before Alfred gets home and if I'm rushed, I'll be tired and short tempered. One in the family, tired out, is enough. The wonderful feeling of kinship with the earth and nature, the realization that God is in everything everywhere, and we are free to seek Him out, must be held to talk about and ponder over when we are alone. It brings to mind something I read: "God said I am the Truth. He did not say I am what you choose to believe." Here in the soil, then, we must find the truth.

What we believed to be right practice in tilling the soil, couldn't be right or it would not lose its fertility. This farm, once fertile and rich, produces now so little that a family, even a small one, with any desire for some of the luxuries and conveniences of our civilization could not possibly eke out an existence on it without becoming so exhausted and beaten that all their finer qualities would disappear. Thus come ugliness, squalor and misery, slums in the country. We would not look at this picture, yet it could be, and is accepted by many. We must not become over-tired physically, that our minds might continue to search out ways and means; that we might read the lessons we see in the soil, and use the intelligent scientific knowledge of others at our disposal. We are not blind, then let us use our sight and, do what, if not our own intelligence, then that of others so freely available, tells us.

It is said that Canada consumes between 80 and 85 per cent of its agricultural products. With the population increase maintained, agriculture must keep pace if we are to continue exporting food products. But what if we let our arable land lose its fertility? Our soil produced a far higher yield per acre fifty years ago than it does on the average today. Why? I wonder if we have practised the Golden Rule in our agriculture, "give to the soil what you would have it give to you."

Our farm had been left to starve; in fact, when we came to it, the last injustice it could suffer was in progress, live stock eating the last effort of the soil. If not given improved cultivation, it would become completely barren. Nature through the years would bring back the forest, a percentage of which should not have been cleared away when it first came into human hands. Our pasture, after the first month, dried up, since the cattle were now on it. It was taken over by devil's paint brush, mullein and daisies, with iris and swale grass in the low marshy spots by the stream. Only the cedars held back moisture and the spring, feeding into a sunken barrel provided water for the cattle all summer.

Our outlook was grim, in spite of the fascination life in the country held for us. We dared not face squarely what seemed inevitable.

Look at the grain! In spite of the fertilizer, the yield was low, the plants sick. And our capital resources as well as physical, were stretched to breaking point. Something had to give. We were too terribly busy with our routine chores and daily problems to think very far ahead. Alfred worked with a neighbour and two others going from one farm to the next to draw and thresh the grain. This kept him away from work he should be doing at home. For the better part of three weeks, rainy days didn't permit one to accomplish much at home. In that period, two fine days were more than enough for our threshing.

I was excited and important. Feeding the threshing team, anxious to make a reputation as a good cook that Alfred would be proud of, I planned the meals carefully, submitting my menus to Alfred for his approval. He quite enjoyed my serious approach to four ordinary meals and respected my concern by giving it his attention. "Just add a big dish of apple sauce each meal and they will be fine, don't worry."

I made a big bowl of apple sauce, and the mistake of putting cereal dishes at each place to eat it in. The apple sauce which I had felt sure would do for two meals was cleared up in one, plus a full course dinner of roast beef, two vegetables besides potatoes, two kinds of pies cut in quarters, bread and butter and pickles. I'd started at six, and baked all morning, juggling pies and pie shells with only three plates to bake them on. The food and the cook were ready sharp at twelve, hot and steaming. The men, dusty and tired, washed round clean circles on their faces to prove they were white men, and filed to the table, silent with fatigue and hunger. In fifteen minutes flat all I'd spent hours preparing was cleaned up, a little crust of bread wiped over their plates and they were gone again. I ate a hasty lonely meal from the corner of a littered table, as I viewed with jaundiced eyes the dishes and cooking utensils I had to wash before starting in with the same kind of meal all over again, except the meat, which would be cold. And besides, I'd have the chickens to feed, water to carry from the barn because Alfred would be too busy today, and the cows to bring in.

Nip, the colt Alfred bought with Peggy, was a devil. We got a halter on him, but he could not be trained. He was mean, mischievous and nasty, so he spent the entire summer in the pasture. That would have been quite all right if he hadn't concocted a little game to infuriate me.

He would come docilely up through the pasture with the cows, no matter how I tried to manoeuvre him away from them, as I gathered them into one place and assured them that this was milking time. When we reached the entrance to the lane, halfway to the barn. Nip would scatter the cows with his antics, sending them running in all directions. Tired, half tearful, cursing as I'd never done before, I would race over the hummocks and through the hollows in mad pursuit, and bring them finally up the lane. Then I'd have to hurry faster with the supper for the men.

The run was poor, the straw dirty, but it was our own grain in the bins and a certain exhilaration possessed us. Alfred was all smiles, in spite of his fatigue. Talking with regular farmers, asking questions, stimulated him, and I had done myself proud.

"No one could provide a better meal." Alfred smiled happily as he said it.

After a sponge bath in the kitchen, we mounted the ugly old staircase, because of its yellowing paint fondly called The Golden Stairs, to bed, oblivion and rest.

Another day, and our threshing was finished, though Alfred had yet many days to put in on the other farms.

After the threshing machine pulled out, and the farmers followed it, I hurried to the barn to stand with Alfred and look at our first harvest. Mows half full, granary about the same, yet this barn had been built to be filled to capacity in earlier years. What a story it told, and how many more farms in this rich country of ours tell the same. When will we have to join the many nations who import food products because they can't produce enough to feed their own?

Our problem now was to feed ourselves, and it was a big one. Tonight we were too tired to give our apprehension much thought and tomorrow Alfred would be away most of the day. Thus, bewildering problems are relegated to another time and the business of the day absorbs all our attention and energy.

A piece of summer fallow done behind a walking plough produced for me the material for a beautiful picture if I had had the ability and time to paint it; but for Alfred, behind the plough, a feeling of physical inadequacy to cope with the work involved in farming, filled his thoughts.

Coming home from threshing, the first question Alfred always asked was: "What's new?"

One night I met him with, "There is a skunk in the trap just inside the doors on the barn floor and it is still alive."

"Oh, my God! How will I ever get rid of it!" We had no gun. "Go call the real estate agent. Tell him he can buy the farm for a dollar," shouted Alfred as resolutely he strode towards the barn and a problem that had to be solved.

With a long pole that could not have been more unwieldy, Alfred lifted the door latch and as was its wont, the door swung immediately open. The dozing or dazed skunk stirred, Alfred still had the sliding doors to open. The trap chain was finally loosened from its mooring with the long pole, and the skunk started across the field dragging the trap behind it. Alfred put a nail in the end of the pole, hooked it in the chain, and dragged the skunk to the gravel pit where, with the only means he had available, he quickly ended its misery. He didn't get sprayed, but the pungent perfume filled the air in our vicinity with smothering intensity.

"I can't treat even a skunk like that; I'll have to get a gun," said Alfred.

Not even the loss of countless baby chickens could make us feel completely heartless. We got a gun.

The chores were drudgery that night. We finished up as quickly as our tired bodies would allow, then sponge baths in the kitchen and to bed with heavy steps. It was an effort to hold the lighted lamp steady to light our way. Even the extreme heat under an uninsulated, low, sloping roof could not keep us from sleep tonight. Blowing the lamp out, I whisper, "God bless you, darling," but Alfred is asleep, exhausted.

Another day. While harvesting was still in progress, the pigs, penned in the orchard and growing bigger every day, started digging their way out. Alfred had hastily fixed their pen many times. One got out and I could not corner it. They don't have to be greased to be slippery, I find. When Alfred came home, we both tried, darting all over the place trying to outma- noeuvre the wily little beast. I don't know how it happened, but I swooped as it darted past me and caught it by a hind leg, screaming in incredulous surprise to Alfred, "I've got it! I've got it." I realized instantly that I couldn't hold it for long. It must have weighed about 80 lbs. Alfred, startled by my feat, was frozen still for an instant, then diving to relieve me he sprained his thumb, arriving just in time to catch the wriggling porker almost out of my grasp, and lift him back to his pen.

The family voted me Champion Pig Catcher. The title has never since been contested.

A nursery man came along selling dreams. We bit off a large one. One thousand raspberry canes. They would be a good cash crop. And a few favourite apples Alfred could not resist.

It was an unusually hot day when they arrived and we planted them. Alfred worked stripped to the waist, and I couldn't see any reason why I should not have the same exquis- ite experience of air on my hot skin, so I took my shirt off too. We were halfway out in the field working like mad to get our precious raspberry canes into the soil and watered before the roots dried out, when a car turned in our lane. I cowered and literally crawled what seemed Like miles to my shirt. I had it on as the car came over the rise by the house, still able to blush even when it turned out to be just my sister.

"What's the matter," she queried, seeing my face registering a "caught in the act" expression.

"I had my shirt off, and didn't know how I'd get it on again without being seen." After all this was not a nudist colony, and we had to remember that others might be embarrassed, even if we weren't.

The raspberry canes, duly planted and expertly cared for, were like putting money in the bank. I was very careful not to visualize for a moment the work of harvesting the bumper crop and finding a market. This year, I beat the birds to the red currants and made seven glasses of jelly.

The canning machine was wonderful. We made up for low quality in the garden with quantity, and everything not consumed during the summer went into cans for the winter. Nothing was wasted. The corn we canned found its own market. I gave a tin as a bridge prize one night more in fun than anything, but it took care of all the surplus. In fact, we let the buyer set the price. He was in the grocery business and could get his supplies wholesale. He preferred ours for his own use and recommending it to his friends, we got two to three cents more than the retail price without asking for it!

We sold over 400 cans, with plenty for our own use in the cellar, and took in close to one hundred dollars for this cash crop. We were gaining a lot of experience along the way. Canning the corn to sell was doing it the hard way. My brother Matt donated an enamel-topped table to the cause. The flies on our farm didn't know about DDT, so we surprised them and consequently kept the house free of them with no trouble at all. Alfred would cut the kernels off the cobs, I would sterilize cans and fill, then put the cans immediately into a large boiler where we could process thirty-five cans at a time. Tending the fire to keep the water boiling hard for three hours was a job in itself, but we managed.

One night we canned till about two a.m. and I stayed up to keep the processing going. It was like night duty again, only this time I chose to do it. Many times during that night-long vigil over the boiling pots, I thanked Alfred fervently for not wanting me to go back to nursing to help augment our living. This was enough night duty for me. We had two long nights of it, doing the corn when it was at its best. The second night the processing started earlier so we both stayed up. We had cans boiling in everything, this being the last lot. The good old iron stove was covered; steam filled the kitchen. We were so tired. Casting sidelong glances at the chesterfield and studio couch we succumbed. Alfred lay on the mattress of the studio couch on the floor in front of the fireplace, I on the chesterfield. Everything was boiling nicely. We could rest for a few minutes. In a few minutes, we were sound asleep. Then—

"BANG! BANG! BANG!"

We were afraid to look, but oh, so wide awake now.

"If the fire screen had not been up, I would have gone right into the fireplace. I thought it was a bomb!" Alfred said.

One of the smaller pots had boiled dry and three cans of corn exploded. There was corn in the curtains, plastered on the ceiling, and in every corner of the room. It was one horrible mess to clean up at two a.m., after a long day of hard work. It didn't break any windows, but there would be marks of corn instilled in the nice newly painted ceiling till it could be painted again. Something to remind us to stay awake next time.

Neilsons did the ploughing, but we did our own cultivating. Mr. Randall had an old horse he wasn't using, and if we cared to pasture it we could have it till the fall. He'd sell it later for fox meat. Poor beast, when its usefulness was over, there was no place for it.

Cultivating on the slopes was hard work for horses, but with four pulling it wouldn't be so bad for any one of them. Alfred hitched them up and made a round, then I was to take over. Coming down the slope, he raced them to show me how easy it would be driving a four-horse team. I was as nervous as a kitten, and as anxious to do it as any young lad might be. Alfred watched while I made a round and, all bravado, I too raced the horses down the slope shouting,

"Ben Hur, here I come!"

The exhilaration, the power, the control, I felt was wonderful. With full consideration for the horses, they were rested frequently.

"Don't let them get hot," Alfred admonished, "then you will know it's not too hard for them."

He'd lengthened Randall's ties to ease his pull. Each horse according to its ability pulled the cultivator and I, proud of my accomplishment, guided them over the field in which we intended to kill the twitch grass or else—

We cultivated that field sixteen times, and felt quite righteous about it. We were doing something. We were working hard. What we were really doing, we learned much later, thus proving to us that hard work alone does not make a good farmer. He first needs to know what he should do.

We worked our land according to the methods commonly used in the district. We suffered the disappointment of not getting a milk contract, and had a poor crop which necessitated selling four heifers and four cows, because it would not be economically sound for us to buy in hay and straw that second winter. We also sold six calves. Some of them, heifers, we would have liked to keep. This kept money dribbling in to aid the "Doings" when the purse got slim. The gravel pit did pay the taxes, as the man said it would, and for this we were grateful.

My worries were nothing compared to Alfred's. Though we had no conveniences, he did the nicest, most thoughtful thing he could for my comfort. He built a privy off the back shed. The luxury of not having to plough through deep snow or keep a path cleared to the wee house out back was wonderful, and I was deeply grateful. The hard work, with the worry of keeping things going, kept Alfred quiet and apprehensive. Life on the farm came close to becoming a drudgery all the time to both of us.

On into the night we would talk and plan. Alfred's trip to London for his yearly check-up added to our worries. They wanted to operate on his feet again. We had been told about a good place to have boots made to measure, and Alfred was advised by our own doctor to try this first. It took a lot of persuasion and real nagging on my part to persuade him a year later to do this. Spending money on himself was just not the thing to do, thought Alfred. He would rather go to town at Christmas or on my birthday and empty the purse buying gifts for me.

The lowest ebb came in midwinter, with not too much income, the uncertainty his feet kept him in, and the rationing of fodder. An ad in the local paper started Alfred thinking. He could sell the back fifty, work in town, keep a few pigs, chickens and cows, and sell small fruits. I said nothing. He was the breadwinner and must do it the best way he could. That I wasn't happy about it was due perhaps to my dislike of change, or more likely because I wanted us to succeed on our hundred acres when no one who knew us expected us to.

A neighbour was looking for more land. He wanted to expand. This was our opportunity, so Alfred offered him the back fifty, which included the permanent pasture, or wasteland as it could be better named, and the cedar grove with two fields, one of which we had seeded down. I hated to think we would not have the first hay crop from it, so much hope had gone into planting it.

After due consideration our neighbour turned the offer down. So now we were stuck with it. Sink or swim; sell the farm, lock, stock and barrel, or make the best of it!

There was no further question about what we would do. Make the best of it, of course. Privately, I think, we were both glad.

Alfred's feet must have been feeling a little better, or perhaps it was because we made a nice profit on feeding pigs, and the chickens weren't doing too badly. Money kept coming in. We managed well with what we had. Because of the friendliness we felt for this soil, or because it was as run down as we felt, and misery likes company, we named our place "Friendship Farm," and decided to stay.

—Courtesy Dept. of Public Relations, O.A.C., Guelph.

Top: Showing the result of soil culture on poor land. Red clover, alfalfa, brome and orchard grass for hay and silage and pasture.

Bottom: Margaret Leatherbarrow feeding the pullets.

Top: Grass silage, hay, straw and even grain for threshing can be picked up from the windrow by the McKee Pneumatic Harvester.

Bottom: Dry hay being unloaded at the barn by the McKee Harvester with the aid of only one man.

CHAPTER 8

"Friendship Farm!" The name was like a magic key opening a door of understanding between ourselves and the soil. We were conscious of a strong, intangible power attracting us, and demanding of us the best effort we could muster. I was glad that Alfred didn't get a job in town or sell the back fifty, and I think he was too. We never mentioned selling out.

With afternoon quiet filling the sleepy kitchen, I sat by the window looking down towards the cedar grove and Alfred cutting dead wood in the depleted wood-lot beyond. There were a number of dead elms and hemlocks, and our fireplace could be a hungry monster on long winter evenings.

An idea strikes me. Hurriedly I push the kettle forward on the stove, then get into my barn coat and boots to go gather the eggs. When I get back to the house the kettle is boiling. While the coffee perks I make sandwiches and, filling the thermos, I load my big pockets and start down through the fields, sinking in the deep snow, climbing over the little bit of rail fence showing above the drifts, to Alfred. It would be a surprise picnic, much nicer than something expected of me or planned ahead. Stopping to rest on his axe and look towards the house where he could see the friendly smoke rising from the chimney in the winter air, Alfred was surprised to see me waving, to assure him there was nothing wrong.

Silently, alone, he had been planning things. Now we could talk them over, while the ideas were fresh in his mind.

"I've coffee and sandwiches in my pockets."

"Good. Let's go up in the cedars, out of this wind."

We were surrounded by the stillness of the white, rolling landscape. The ruins of a burnt-out stone house and some ancient apple trees were the only sign that humans had been near. We climbed over the stumps to the stillness of the grove.

It was like entering a great cathedral; each tree reaching a cone to the sky, its branches fringed and heavy with snow.

There was no wind here. We were snug and warm, sitting on a fallen tree trunk, eating sandwiches and drinking steaming coffee. The stillness is like a benediction. The trees and shrubs seem watchful, waiting to see what new atrocity man will perpetuate to mar his heritage. We don't feel foreign to this place, and conviction grows that all will be well. Home is on this land. Here we are in our Kingdom. Here we find our God by seeking for the truth revealed in the soil it is our privilege to husband. We aren't fighting nature, but forging a bond of friendship that will deepen with the years.

Unwilling to break the spell of peacefulness and oneness that our surroundings placed on us, Alfred shouldered his axe and crosscut saw and, hand in hand, we returned to the house.

A warm, sunny day brought lots of planning. Alfred was facing everything squarely. He could not, immediately, do everything that he wanted to do, but this did not stop him from doing everything he possibly could, the best way he knew how. He didn't rely on what the neighbours did, or what he knew himself, but read all he could find on field husbandry, feeding and soils. We'd talk about what he'd read until it was accepted as the right thing for us to do, or rejected as impractical.

From the barnyard, looking over the field that had given us such a pitifully poor crop the summer of 1947, we planned to seed it down. Legumes were good for the soil; so, as it wouldn't grow grain, we'd better try to improve the fertility by seeding it. Besides, we had to improve our hay crop anyway. I had some romantic notion that once we had seeded down the entire farm it would really belong to us. It had been like an orphan whom, up till now, no one had wanted.

The big purchase in equipment on which we would allow ourselves to spend the "Doings" was to be a binder and seeder. It was hoped both would turn up at sales, which they did. It was January when Alfred bought the binder. Perhaps it went cheaper then because no one felt urgently in need of one at that time of year. We went for it with the team and sleigh, hoping to get it back without harm over the snow-covered rutty roads. I sat wrapped up in blankets in the straw, holding a dog the owner didn't want, and found in holding its shivering frightened body a warmth of feeling towards it which I had never felt for a dog before.

So Pal came to us in the winter, a stray dog, but so intelligent. He knew just what to do to keep the pigs away when Alfred was cleaning their pen, and the exact moment they could be herded in again. He was marvellous with the horses, and how I wished we'd had him in the summer when kindheartedness rather than better judgment let the horses out to pasture at night after work, and we raced all over the pasture trying to get the wily beasts into the stable. Come spring, Pal wandered away for three days, and I welcomed him back as one would a prodigal son. Once again he disappeared, never to return. I used to call and call and peer into the distance. Once, seeing a dog that looked like him, I called and called, but it belonged to a neighbour.

During the Christmas holidays that year, we were asked by the secretary of our little country school if we would clean it. Wanting to be good neighbours and follow the customs of the farmers about us, we agreed to perform the task.

Hitching a horse to the cutter soon after the morning chores were done, we loaded it up with a boiler, pails, brooms, dusters, mops, and soap, and piled in. It was a lovely drive. The snow was so deep we went right over the fences as we crossed the fields. The heavy blankets Alfred and I had sewn together our first winter came in handy this day, to keep our horse warm while we scrubbed and cleaned and sweated it out in the school-house. I had always thought it a small building, until I started to scrub my way across its dirty floor. When it was finished we didn't need to tell each other, "never again."

Living in or near a village is wonderful. You have identity. Everybody knows or knows of you, and shows varying interest in what you do. Though more critical, they are also more tolerant than city people. The grapevine is healthy and hearty; a great institution that whiles away the dull moments, giving them colour and zest. One learns things about oneself one had never known before.

We have a friend, a merchant in town. When Alfred goes in his shop, he always has some smiling, interested query, based often on some tit-bit he has heard. Conversation will go something like this:

"How's everything going, Alf?"

"Fine. Couldn't be better."

Always the same reply.

"You are no farmer," retorts our friend.

"Why?"

"Farmers always complain. If it's not the weather, it's the prices. If the grain crop was good, it was bad for the land, took too much out of it. Conditions must be bad to be a good farmer."

They laugh together, and we make a date to play bridge one night soon.

Cleaning stables was taking more physical exertion than Alfred could muster. Day after day he kept to himself, pondering continuously on ways and means whereby the work could be made easier. During the winter the stabling got full attention. As spring advanced, the barn furniture had to be juggled about, so each bit of equipment, as it was needed, would be handy.

"I think we could go into the moving business," I'd suggest, after juggling a binder, hay loader, rake or seeder about. "A grand piano would be child's play." I felt like the powerful Katrinka when we started, and a shadow of myself when the job was complete.

Poor Alfred, with only me to help! I don't know just why we didn't talk more of a change, but once the back fifty was not sold, we never again suggested any different way of life; just doggedly carried on, each wondering how long we'd last and what would come next.

Perhaps the day Alfred would decide to talk it over with me, a new calf would be born to warm our hearts toward our little kingdom, or the hens would outdo themselves laying an above-average quota of eggs. The mail might have brought in a pig cheque. Anyway, we'd feel affluent for a day and, carried on its crest, plan optimistically for tomorrow, our fatigue forgotten momentarily.

We kept books from the beginning. At the end of 1947, our poultry had given us a better profit than any other enterprise. The pigs came a close second. The dairy lagged far behind, besides being for us the most binding and tedious chore. After Christmas we planned the campaign for 1949. It was to be the year we would seed down as much as we possibly could, to improve our hay crop and soil fertility, and make it possible we hoped to pasture safely more than the dozen head of cattle we had worried about carrying through the winter. We would feed as many pigs as we could, and increase the poultry without extra outlay for equipment by ordering 250 baby chicks in February and 300 in April. I'd have baby chicks to keep me busy and happy all spring, and could hardly wait till the first lot arrived.

The first balmy day that brings promise of spring lifts the spirit and breeds optimism. We shelve our doubts and fears in anticipation of that glorious day when Alfred will hitch the horses and cultivate a piece of ground in preparation for the seeding.

That first sunny warm day finds us hurrying to the granary where Alfred has lugged the fanning mill he got at a sale for $1. Here he has swept clean a bin for our seed, bought last year. This is our own magic gold. With a pail I scoop the grain and dump it in the mill hopper. Alfred turns the wheel at the exact speed that will not blow good grain out with the chaff. My job is much the easier, and Alfred generally has to call "uncle" first. With plenty of time ahead of us, this task doesn't have to be an energy-consuming chore. I can stand for a while at the granary window and look over the countryside that we love, bathed in warm sunshine with here and there a dark spot showing the brown earth where snow has melted. We stop when tired, and gather the eggs. We look in on the placid cattle chewing their cuds, warm and content, then go hand in hand back to the kitchen and mid-morning coffee.

A sale produced the needed seeder for $2, and a wagon box filled with odd bits of machinery needed on a farm for quick repairs. Before Alfred left the sale, he had sold some of the odd pieces for $3.25. The box and all it contained had cost $8. He was pleased as Punch with his purchases that day. He had also bought some bedroom furniture. One day I went to an auction to get a couch for the kitchen, and came home with a lawn-mower, a jug and a bowl. The jug has turned out to be a collector's item, valued close to $20, but I paid ten cents for it. The lawn mower, costing $3, did service for six years. The bowl isn't broken yet. My crowning purchase came when I was sent to buy a grindstone, because Alfred was too busy to go. I came home without the grindstone, of course, but in its place, a horse rasp.

"The auctioneer said it was worth $2.35, and I got it for 35 cents," I explained.

"I'll bet all the farmers there laughed at you."

Weeks later, when the Vet was in to pinch some calves, Alfred asked him to look at Peggy. She wasn't eating.

"If you had told me, I would have brought my rasp. One of her teeth is jagged. It just needs to be filed a bit."

"I have a rasp," said Alfred. My purchase saved us a four-dollar trip.

One cold, sunny day in January, I went with Alfred on top of a load of grain, to the mill two miles away. With a wagon box to put on the sleds, there was no danger of the bags rolling off now. I sat up on the horse-blankets we had made from our old patchwork quilt and bags. We knew the horses would have to stand exposed to the elements for some length of time and we wanted them warm.

Sliding over the snow-covered road, we were lulled by the rhythmic motion; plumes of frosty, moisture-laden air spouting from the horses' nostrils. The country was beautiful, filled with muted colour tones under a blanket of snow that turns all the ugly trivia of a farmyard into graceful figures. Old buildings, odd implements, the rail fence corners we pass, form shadows soft and undulating. Off in the distance we spy a neighbour winding his way from barn to house, and wave a greeting. Frost fringes our moist scarves where they cover our chins, and crimson colours our cheeks. Eyes sparkling, sitting shoulder to shoulder, we enjoy to the full every minute of the adventure.

A pot of Boston baked beans, home-made, simmers in the oven, and a pot of home-made vegetable soup stands on the back of the stove, beside the kettle, to tickle our nostrils and whet already ravenous appetites when we get back.

Looking to the spring, one thing was necessary—a faster means of transportation. A 1928 Buick soon came into our possession, and were we ever proud! It was in good running order, and the body didn't look too bad, considering its age. Now we would not have to borrow a neighbour's car when the need arose, and it would not likely consume as much gas as we had bought, filling the gaugeless tank of a borrowed one. Once a week to Broomfield for bridge with Mother and Dad was the extent of our pleasure driving.

Having no milk contract, we sold our Holstein bull. Breeding our cows to a beef bull would be more practical, looking ahead to the steers we would raise. The trips to neighbours with cows for service came at inopportune times, and the cows showed as much individuality as people in their behaviour as they were led down the lane. I always took a stout switch. One would have to be prodded all the way; another would take us there and back in mileage several times over with its antics. We'd laugh and swear and be exasperated as the occasion merited, but never bored.

Soon the trees would begin to show signs of life, the twigs and branches swelling with buds, sap trickling down the trunks of the maples that lined our front lane and the roadside. A faint tinge of green would appear, accompanied by birdsong. The earth, brown and wet with white patches of snow, edged with green where grass was peeping through, made the world look fresh and clean. Expectancy filled the still nippy air. Then we would tap the trees. An evaporator would be rigged up outside, with plenty of wood handy to keep the fire going. We would all be busy.

Alfred hitched Snow White to the stone-boat sleigh he had made. With a large metal barrel, securely tied, we'd go from tree to tree emptying the sap pails. Once, on Alfred's insistence, I rode Snow White. He broke into a trot. Spread-eagled over harness, I bounced along, able only to hold on. For the next week I longed for a cushion each time I sat down. We could have made some money with our syrup if I hadn't given so much away that Spring before the work began.

It was time now to pull on our rubber boots and tour the farm, look at our hay fields, and see how rapidly the ground was drying up. The day would soon be here when, with the barn doors flung wide to allow free circulation of air, our noses covered with masks, we'd mix and mix the sarasan with the grain and bag it preparatory to immediate seeding.

Surely from this fifteen acre field, that we had worked so much in the fall, cultivated sixteen times, tearing at the twitch grass, seeding it down now and fertilizing, we'd get the good grain crop we needed. Now, watching Alfred pacing back and forth behind the seeder I wonder, "Is it worth it? Will he decide to quit? This operation alone must be sheer torture."

The mangels were excellent. I thought the harvesting, like the hoeing and thinning, would never end. One day, rescued from the constant bending when a neighbour stopped to pass the time of day with Alfred, I slumped down behind the wagon, too weary to care where or what I sat on. I was grateful for a respite but I would not let Alfred see I needed it, for he needed it even more than I.

There is no fun in this, I thought. We aren't living. We are struggling to survive. Each day's work kept us on the go, early and late. Something had to be figured out.

If someone had come along then and offered a reasonable price for the farm, we would have sold it. But the farm was too well known as worn-out. The raspberry canes were sick. I picked barely enough to put on our breakfast cereal. The strawberries were abundant, but so were the weeds, and after we had picked all the fruit new plants were set out in a new garden plot in the orchard.

I suppose everything looked seedy. It did to my uncle, my father and a friend who called one day when Alfred was away helping on a neighbouring farm. As though I were not there, the farm, our plan of operation, and the stock were so well and ably criticized that my anger rose, if only in defence of those poor cattle. These men relegated to low grade the animals grazing nearby, and unable to answer in their own defence. We were pronounced unthrifty and bound to fail.

I was livid with rage. We had put forth our very best effort, and it was taking all the strength we had. I felt I had been knocked down and kicked insensible, even though they meant well. But it may have had some influence in strengthening our determination to find an easier, better way of farming, with leisure for play.

We paid a visit to the Agricultural College in Guelph. Digging up several of the sick-looking raspberry canes, Alfred took them there for analysis. We learned that the canes had a disease carried over a two-year period, and would either die or not be thrifty.

This accurate information made it possible to get a rebate on our investment and assured us that we need not give up the project entirely.

Time, during the spring, summer and fall, is always of utmost importance. No time clock or noon whistle could be more exacting than the necessity to have dinner ready the moment Alfred came in. It took such a lot of time harnessing and tending the horses before he could get back to the job at hand. I kept on the run to be always on hand when needed, and have meals on time too. How easy it would be to let discord arise when both of us were tired and felt a little justifiable sense of martyrdom. How we kept our sense of proper values, I will never know. Perhaps it was because we both worked at it, not leaving everything to that magic word "love" that is expected to surmount all obstacles, with no help from the people who wish to enjoy its benefits. Our affection for one another was adult, and our desire to keep it was sincere. No wall of misunderstanding could be allowed to grow between us; nothing could be allowed to be of greater importance than our understanding and sympathy for each other.

We bought a second-hand hay loader that gave us not too much trouble, considering. The drive chain would break frequently. Alfred had a few links in his "Treasure," but we always hunted for the lost one. It was exasperating to be held up this way, when we were trying so hard to keep to an easy quota of five loads of hay a day. If the weatherman, to whom we listened with attention every day, promised rain on the morrow, Alfred wouldn't have to ask me if I minded; we just knuckled down and worked to get all the hay ready, in under cover.

"There is no use working like this and getting just exercise for the cattle," he said.

So he would cut, weatherman permitting, as much as he felt we could put in the barn in one day. Our hay crop was a little better this year. So was the grain, for that matter, but it was still far from being a fair-producing farm. With the harvesting equipment we had, our hay went into the barn in the best condition it could. Alfred read a lot about drying, and when it should be cut, and what happened when it was left to the ravages of the weather. Thanks to the weather report each day, we were able to feed our cows with well-saved hay.

Seeing the new equipment on display in the stores of implement dealers, Alfred said that he wanted to buy a seeder as soon as possible; one on which he could ride. He also wanted a side-delivery rake. These we dreamed of. They would make work easier and eliminate the running repairs that took so much time.

There were just two days' threshing on our farm that fall, and, as I had had my initiation the year before, I was able to take it in my stride. When it was over, our barn looked a little healthier than the year before, but far from being filled to capacity.

My birthday in August that year was one of the happiest I've ever had. Our son Jim was now beginning to make his presence felt in all the activities of the farm. August is the busiest time of the year for us, but Alfred bundled Jim into the car; took the purse with all the "Doings," and sailed off to town, leaving me at home in a flurry of excitement. I baked a cake and fixed it up with all the trimmings. Called to the orchard, I found Jim perched atop a basket filled with straw. Ordered to fish in the straw, I brought up all manner of little things like tooth brushes, chocolate bars and—hitting something hard—a Coleman iron! What luxury! There was also a high kitchen chair, that I might sit at my work.

By November our little family settled down, and we prepared for a quiet winter of serious planning and studying for drastic changes in our methods of farming.

We went to Toronto for a gala weekend during the winter. It turned out to be a major expedition. At forty miles an hour, the jalopy was literally flying. It could not have been more draughty and with no heater we had to wrap up in plenty of warm clothing. Our teeth chattered, if not from the cold, from the bumpy, snow-covered roads. I believe the springs were considered in good condition. They kept us in constant agitation, anyway. When we arrived, Alfred asked Daisy which house she'd like the car parked in front of for the weekend. She didn't dislike anyone that much, so we parked it in the rear of her own, and pretended it didn't belong to us, each time we drove out in her own deluxe model. It was fun renewing our association with electric lights and a bathtub. I would have been quite content to spend the weekend in the bathroom. Not being chief cook and bottlewasher for a couple of days was a luxury in itself, particularly when you were extremely well fed. Grim reality returned when we started home again. The dim lights of our car commanded no respect from on-coming motorists, and although we know these old models are a menace on the highway, it was the best we could afford. Drivers aren't courteous unless they are compelled to be, we found. I doubt if one oncoming car dimmed its lights for us. By the time we reached Clappison's Corners, Alfred was exhausted, so we stopped for coffee. Turning north in a snowstorm, along a less-travelled road, we felt lonely and cold and longed for the security of our little farm house. The holiday was wonderful, so were all the conveniences, but we longed now for home and urged the utmost from the jalopy.

Our winter was a quiet one. The occasional game of bridge helped to break the intensity of Alfred's concentration on his big problem, of how to increase production, how to cut costs and work. I had succeeded in getting him to have the special boots made, and they gave him a degree of comfort he had not known before. Although our farm was the only one along our line without a tractor, it worried us not at all, and Alfred talked of replacing the older horses with younger ones. We hoped for a good hay crop on the sixteen acres we had worked so hard at cultivating. Only one field was to be seeded down this spring with the mixture used on the other fields.

Alfred spent many hours in his favourite blue chair, thinking of the soil, for in it was the secret to our future. He had to find some method whereby we could increase our production. He knew the grass and legume catch on the sixteen acre field was none too good, so he'd try something different on this other. He'd manure it before seeding. That spring the plan went into action.

A friendly neighbour asked what he was doing on this piece of land he was manuring.

"Seeding it down with a grain crop," Alfred answered.

"But man, they top dress in the fall, for new seed."

"I'm manuring in the spring."

"You're all wrong, man."

"We'll see."

It was a dry spring, hard on the new seed, but where Alfred had manured he had a good catch.

No one would concede that he'd been right, but it was the only decent catch of new seed in the district, and on the worst land. Our grain crop increased from 13 bushels to the acre to 30. But the hay crop, except for the 7 acres he had seeded down our first year, where the grass and legumes were well-established, was poor. Our 16 acres produced half a ton of hay to the acre; the new seed we had had such hopes for! A section of land sloping down to the cedars that had produced poorly Alfred summer-fallowed with the intention of sowing fall rye, which would provide needed fall pasture and a cover crop, as well as a green crop to be worked in in the Spring. This winter's reading and thinking had definitely decided him to work towards a grass land programme and cover crops. It looked like a long time before we would accomplish the plan, but once thinking along these lines, Alfred's alert mind was to find a quicker, better way. We were excited about what we were doing now, but it was nothing compared to what lay ahead.

A change came over us. We were not struggling now, doggedly, against tremendous odds in the form of a run-down farm, with run-down equipment, weather and market hazards, and ill-equipped physically to do battle against these odds. Alfred no longer fought the soil for its last ounce of energy. Rather, he lifted it in his cupped hands as a friend, examining its physical qualities; seeking in it what it could produce now, and new ways to revitalize it.

It changed our attitude. Now, when the little turnip plants broke through the soil in long straight rows, and almost overnight disappeared, the victim of aphids, there was no cursing of luck or blank despair. The soil had done its best with what it had. Deficient as it was, grubs and microbes were bound to take over the plants that could not get the nourishment they needed.

The turnips and mangels that year were an economic gamble, and we lost. We had not wanted to decrease our herd any more than we had already, and the roots were to be a supplement to hay. The half-acre of mangels grew, but did not come up to last year's standard. For all the work involved in seeding, hoeing, thinning and harvesting, they were the most expensive crop we grew. The only compensation for the time we spent on them was that they were growing on a piece of land I called the top of the world. Here we could look all around us for miles; over beautiful rolling, wooded landscape, the little squares and oblongs of various colour tones, depicting different crops in varying stages of growth. A tractor moves across the fields so far away one can barely hear it. Perhaps the farmer is ploughing; if so, one sees a ribbon of brown lengthen out behind the almost invisible plough. Cattle grazing, little farm houses dotting the landscape, all the noisy silence of a peaceful summer day under a cloudless sky fill one with peace and contentment. Working here with a poor excuse for a crop, we know it will never happen again; that all this will be different another year. I had even forgotten the day we planted the mangels, when I couldn't keep the horse in the right furrow as I stumbled over the hard chunks of soil, so hard they were like stones, and Alfred behind trying to keep the seeder straight, having more trouble than I.

"Can't you keep it straight?" he'd shout.

"I'm trying my best," I'd reply, almost in tears because the horse stepped on my feet so often. We are quick to forgive each other our shortcomings. Alfred would not have me leading the horse if he were sure enough of his own feet. I knew that.

When it came time to sow the rye, we set out to find the farm where we could buy it, with very little gas in the car and only enough money to pay for the seed. We got lost before we found the farm, and wondered how far we'd get before we'd have to get out and walk. Perhaps the gas gauge wasn't working very well, for we got home all right, travelling some distance on "empty."

It was a dry spring and the new seed suffered everywhere. However, rain came in time to save the grain. Alfred would point out the deficiencies to me and talk about his ideas and plans. He squared off the back twelve acres, pulling out stumps and ploughing with horses land that had never been worked before. A fence row was cleared up and an excuse for a fence taken out. This, too, he ploughed. We put a new fence around the house grounds, making things look a little more cared for. As a fence stretcher, I can give my all for quite a long period, but it's not quite adequate. However, Alfred praised my efforts and it was good doing things together.

Jim, growing older now, would wander farther afield with his father, the idea being that he would help with the fencing. Sharpening pickets, however, soon grew tiresome, so he and his collie, Ace, would go off hunting woodchucks. The little fellow dug in the earth with his hands, just as the dog did with his forepaws. Suddenly Alfred would realize that he was alone, and would call sharply,

"Jim, where are you?"

"Here I are, Daddy." A brown head would pop out of the ground. Thinking of the hunters who, without asking permission, roamed our fields, and of what that little brown head would look to them on their groundhog hunt filled me with fear and resentment. Why should our son be deprived of the freedom of his own land to satisfy trespassers?

"Run fast for home if you see or hear hunters, Jim," we told him.

When even the orchard lost its safety, we had had enough. "No Hunting" signs were posted, to return to us the right to roam with safety over our rolling hills.

As Jim acquired playmates who didn't know that snakes were useful and wanted in the garden, it was hard for him not to follow the leader and stone the odd one for the delight they felt in their power over the harmless reptile. We were fortunate to find a female with her young, to demonstrate to the boys a little sympathy for parenthood in nature. So even snakes aren't killed on Friendship Farm.

Haying time came and went. We managed, as always, alone, cutting what could be drawn in in one day, and following the weather report to guide our cutting. It was heartbreaking the acreage we covered to get one load of hay. It averaged a half ton to the acre on the field we had spent so much time cultivating sixteen times, accomplishing a destruction of soil structure and nothing of value. Every little bit of hay was carefully raked up. We would need it all, for we had half a dozen young heifers we had raised; our first to come in, in the winter. Seven acres of hay beyond this piece that had been seeded down our first year we found better. The orchard grass and alfalfa were well established, but it would not be enough. Standing by the barn with Alfred watching the pretty heifers grazing not far off, I felt a great surge of pride in these, our very own livestock. Each one had a name, and with most of them I'd been present to watch the miracle of birth and feel the wonder of mother love in the animal kingdom.

There were a few young steers, also our own, among them. They would not be so easy to sell, because most farmers bought larger ones as feeders for the winter. No, the heifers would bring the best price and something had to go.

"There is no money in dairy cattle without a milk contract," Alfred said. "Besides, it's far too much work for us. I spend five hours a day doing chores. It's all out of proportion to what I make."

He was right, I knew. These hard, long hours of work were taking all he had and more. Even the promise of less work in the field, and improved crops seemed far away, a dream to two work-weary people. Alfred's clear thinking and almost brutal cutting down on inefficient production made no allowances for sentiment here.

"The heifers will have to go."

"Don't let me see them loaded on the truck, then," I answered quietly.

We would soon be out of dairy cattle entirely, embarked on a new and different practice in agriculture. We were gambling everything, with no companion farmer in our vicinity doing the same to share our worries and conjectures. We were alone.

It was at this time I had a fleeting thought of our marriage vows, "For better or for worse," and looking up at the tall thin figure beside me, face pale under its summer tan, shoulders drooping in fatigue, lips tight and drawn, I was more aware than ever of his conflict, and knew that come what may we stand together. Although ignorant about farming, I could at least give moral support and encouragement. That's what I married him for, to help, not hinder, and although I did manage to miss seeing my beloved heifers go, I made no mention of them at any time. I had learned that sentimentality had to give place to common sense, and we would both find ourselves doing this all our farming lives.

Autumn came, the grain bins were fuller, the hay mows about the same. We wondered how long it had been since this barn was filled to capacity, as the agent said it had been.

CHAPTER 9

I have heard it said that good can never come from evil. I suppose it depends a lot on what one calls evil. One day in the early spring of 1949, I had just passed through the upper hall when the ceiling fell. And we had every penny allocated to something important on the farm.

I swept it up, and we ignored the ceiling quite well for a day or two. Then one night, looking at it in the dark, we saw stars! No wonder we had been cold in winter. The summer is the time to fix that, but Alfred found the shingles so old and rotten that patching would be of no use; besides he couldn't stand heights to do it. He had a dislike for borrowing, but we had to have a roof before winter, and there was not enough ready cash to pay for one. So, for the first time, he borrowed money from the bank for something that would not bring returns, and we had a new roof put on, and the house insulated as well. We fixed the question of meals for the roofers at the beginning. Alfred told the contractor we didn't provide meals, so I was able to watch with delight the nice new asphalt shingles going on, with nary a care in the world as to what the workmen ate or where they ate it.

A bank loan for something that would not bring a financial yield, at a time when we were breaking away completely from the tried methods of farming, weighed heavily on our minds. The unprofitable heifers had to go, when we could get our best price for them. Our profits had to come from chickens and pigs. To get extra income from the chickens, we decided to sell hatching eggs. For our new programme we must squeeze every cent we could from what we had. Fortunately the pigs were a good paying proposition. Alfred liked feeding them, although he had not yet been satisfied with the thriftiness of any lot he bought for feeding. Often we talked of keeping brood sows, but any we could have kept were never quite good enough to suit him.

It was in March, 1950, that a neighbour who had just bought a new tractor, and wanted to sell his old one, made Alfred a very good offer which I urged him to take.

"How can I? We need that money."

"Just sit down and figure it out. You need the tractor to make your work easier."

He figured it out. The deal was made, and as a result we owned a tractor and one team of horses instead of two teams.

The plowing had all been done the previous fall with horses, and there was a lot of it. Our friend Custom plowed the fifteen acre field. This was to be the last time any plowing was done, beyond rowing up the mangel ground the following spring, by this expert plowman.

With another neighbour Alfred went to his first Soil and Crop Improvement meeting in Fergus, to hear Dr. Weir from O.A.C. speak on a trip to Europe, from which he had just returned. Dr. Weir said that in Holland the practice has been to draw manure from the stable every day and top dress with it. This was the custom till a man decided he might be losing something of value by doing it this way. He analyzed the manure in the stable, then spread some out in the sun on a moisture-proof fabric so nothing could run off. After twenty-four hours it was analyzed again. He discovered 50 per cent of the nitrogen had vanished on exposure. This changed the practice to working the manure into the soil immediately after spreading it.

Here the practice is to plow manure down so that it is virtually buried, Alfred read. The result is that manure, sod, or trash turned under approximately six inches of earth is compressed into a layer anywhere from one-eighth to one-quarter inch thick. This makes a perfect blotter cutting off the capillary system entirely. Moisture coming up from the sub-soil is blocked, and small seeds are left entirely dependent on rainfall for a lengthy period. Also, by plowing, a fine silt is put on top, almost entirely void of organic matter and subject to baking, hardening and cracking, with no insulation for the soil against heat.

A heavy spring rain that will normally supply enough moisture for three or four weeks' growth remains on the surface of plowed ground for three to four days, most of it finding its way to ditches and low ground. The first downpour seals off the fine soil and you have ninety per cent run off.

Sitting in our living-room before a pleasant fire, Alfred tells me what he has found out by reading about different fields and their slopes under different states of cultivation. We remember the barren knolls, all gravel and light soil, and the gushing stream in spring that runs from a neighbour's fields across our own to the lowland of the swamp. The gully in the mangel ground which we left bare this winter we discovered, come spring, verified the reasonableness of the article Alfred had been reading. We also had the knowledge gained by seeing the good catch of new seed when Alfred who had broken with custom, cultivated immediately after manuring, just prior to seeding down. All the other farmers in the district were complaining they had very poor catches of new seed that year because of the exceptionally dry weather. We feel good. Alfred's theories, arrived at through constant reading and checking his own crops, are well founded.

"Never again will I leave a field bare over winter," Alfred vowed, as he read on.

By using a one-way disc you can do the work three times as fast, which means less cost and, instead of burying anything, you mix it in with the top six inches of soil, this, when compacted, leaves your capillary system joined to the surface of the soil, and, after a dry day it can be noticed there is moisture on the surface in the morning. It is also a good insulation against heat, and where you have ninety per cent run off by ploughing you have at least eighty-five per cent saturation in disced ground, because every bit of straw and root stalk acts as a drain into the soil. There is enough trash left on top of the soil to prevent shattering by a heavy downpour. Instead of getting moisture for three or four days, you have it for three or four weeks, when most needed.

Alfred had seen also what wind can do to the bare, dry fields. The day he drove to the neighbour's to go to the Soil and Crop Improvement meeting, an exceptionally strong wind storm was blowing clouds of top soil from every open field along the road. The farmers were losing thousands of dollars worth of top soil, and could do nothing immediate to stop it. We were beginning to feel that a farmer did not have to be fatalistic about nature. The wind and rain need not be totally destructive. We could do something definite about it, and intended to.

Alfred shopped for a one-way disc, and found one on a nearby farm, little used. The owner was glad to sell it, as he had little use for it in his method of working the land.

"We won't have much meat in the locker, and nothing coming on that we can butcher," Alfred remarked as we discussed our new spring programme. "I'd like to buy a lot of fertilizer, and we can't buy meat and it too."

"Buy the fertilizer. We can eat eggs and vegetables. It's everything for the land this year," I said.

We were of one mind, well content, excited and not a little apprehensive. I am told that you can make figures prove anything. Theories and ideas on paper or in men's minds can fall far short when put into practice. For us, the die was cast. All or nothing. We'd sink or swim. So I laughed my worries away again.

I remembered the day in the heat and bustle of summer when Alfred, away all day threshing, returned at night with hopeful eyes and the tired query, "Anything new?"

"I can't get Helen to go into the stable. I brought her up three times with the other cows, and when she gets to the barnyard gate she dashes back past me and is away." I was almost in tears, angry and tired.

Alfred went up the ramp of the barn and called.

"Co Boss! Co Boss!" It was her master's voice. He had saved her life. In a moment, as we stood silently watching, an answering bawl came back from behind the cedar grove. Helen, rounding the cedars, ran to the stable and her stall.

I had been snubbed by a cow. Perhaps, for my self-esteem, it was just as well we were going out of dairy cattle.

Nor were we to be tormented any more by our horses. We could not resist giving them their freedom at night. After their long hard day of work we turned them out to pasture, thus assuring ourselves of perhaps several hours hard running to bring them in. The year Alfred had such a lot of ploughing to do he knew the older horses couldn't handle it, and as horses were cheap that summer, we sold the old ones and bought four more, all brothers, aged one, two, three, and four. They made a dark and a light team. Peggy had been expert at pawing down fences. Bill was still better. He kept gaps open in the pasture fence for the cattle to get through, and I kept my weight down running after them. All I had to do was go out to the pasture with my pockets full of apples, give one to each horse, turn back to the barn, and have four horses abreast at my back right across the field to the stable yard, where Alfred would be waiting with halters. Jack became impatient once when I wasn't feeding out the apples fast enough to please him. He caught my arm in his mouth and shook it, gently enough, but it left quite a bruise.

We had chased them over five farms once, finally cornering them near a barn. We each led two of them down the road home. I was tired and frightened because they were so spirited. In every field corner on the road stood neighbour's horses, whinnying to ours. Not knowing their language, I couldn't tell what new mischief they might be up to before I got them home.

It was time to change from horses. We had both had enough.

Daisy came for Christmas. Alfred couldn't get the car to go when he started out to get Mother and Dad. We hitched the tractor to it with me at the wheel, but the brakes were frozen solid, and the heavy old Buick just wouldn't budge. Every other day the car would go, but not on Christmas Day. Nevertheless, all enjoyed themselves. It was Daisy's first overnight visit in winter, and she wasn't bothered a bit by the bedroom china and outside plumbing. In fact she wanted to return in January for a longer visit, and did.

Right after Christmas we decided something had to be done about the upstairs hall and our bedroom, so we started taking paper off again. I was glad there wasn't any to come off the hall ceiling. They aren't big rooms, but we worked day and night, scraping, wetting, and scraping again. Fortunately, the floors could not be hurt, so we sloshed the water on. Daisy was to return on the 20th. On the 18th, about two a.m., it was finished.

We had found out why, in winter, if the north wind blew, we had a sizeable snow drift across one corner of the bedroom.

Here, when the paper came off, we found a large hole, stuffed with rags and papers that had been the nest of rats and mice between us and the wide open spaces in a stone wall. Perry came out. They mixed mortar in the kitchen, where it would be warm beside the kitchen stove, and patched up the walls and ceiling. The drab rooms were made clean and bright, with blue and peach in the bedroom—a vain attempt on my part, to catch the sunset, and provide a contrasting colour for the lilacs that bloomed outside one window in the spring. The hall we painted white. Our Golden Stairs, changed to pearly whiteness, now mounted to a bedroom where it was no longer necessary to dress up to sleep. Insulation, a new roof and plaster had given us undreamed of comfort. We revelled in the luxury of warmth.

The annual convention of the Ontario Crop Improvement Association was being held in Toronto on January 18, 19 and 20. Alfred made arrangements to go with a neighbour for one day, the 19th when Mr. Louis Bromfield was to be the guest speaker at dinner. They started off early in the morning. The pigs were on self-feeders. There was hay on the barn floor. I could manage the chores.

From the front living-room window I watched Alfred drive off at daybreak. With a busy day ahead of me, the house to shine and polish and baking to do, so I'd have more free time with Daisy and the chores, there was no time to feel lonely. So the day vanished. The guest room was as attractive and comfortable as I could make it; a bath mat beside the bed, so Daisy wouldn't have to step on cold linoleum. (Besides we had no bathroom for the mat). A white linen bedspread I'd embroidered in Italian cutwork and edged with linen lace I'd knit in the lonely years when I dreamed of being a homemaker, just suited the old fashioned room with its pink bedroom china relics from my grand-parents' home.

By midnight I had finished. The kitchen floor was scrubbed, bread was rising behind the stove, cookies and cake filled all my tin containers. The menus were planned and written out, so I wouldn't have to think about what I had to do before each meal.

I put a lamp in the living-room window, and listened with straining ears as the minutes turned into hours and my imagination took me through torments of apprehension. I went back and forth from window to kitchen, putting the kettle forward and pulling it back, so it wouldn't boil dry. I didn't want to have to go to the barn again for a pail of hard water, and there was just enough in it for breakfast.

At last, at two a.m., a ribbon of light penetrated the darkness along the road, growing brighter as the car approached and disappearing into darkness again as the car stopped and turned at our laneway. How glad I was the road was not well-travelled, for I would have watched each ribbon cross my vision and vanish, hope rising and falling with each one, and be exhausted when Alfred did reach home. Instead, joy filled the house. I rushed to put the coffee on and be at the door playfully wielding the rolling pin.

Whose eyes shone the most, I don't know. After our greeting, Alfred told me how it surprised the men who drove him home to see a light in our window. One asked in amazement, "Will your wife be waiting up for you?" "Yes," said Alfred, "and what's more, she'll have the coffee ready."

The men were both bachelors; perhaps, Alfred thought, it might give them ideas.

We weren't sleepy. This was the time for Alfred to tell me what he'd learned. "Then I'll remember it perfectly," he said, and I was an enthusiastic listener. We didn't know what time it was when we went to bed, or care.

"We all separated at the coliseum and I never left the building," he began. "Went from one lecture to another. At lunch, I stood in the doorway looking for a good table to listen to the speakers and a waiter approached and asked, 'Are you for the head table, sir?' Wow!"

I giggled. My good-looking distinguished husband in his navy blue suit that didn't shine because he hadn't enough opportunity to wear it, perhaps.

"No," Alfred had replied. "I just want a table where I can hear the speakers well."

The lecturers had filled his mind with thoughts and ideas all day, and it all culminated in an enthusiastically received talk by Mr. Bromfield at night.

"I'm going to tell you," Mr. Bromfield said, "how to make twice as much money with half as much work." Everyone sat forward and listened attentively. "Farmers don't need floor

prices and subsidies," he said, no doubt causing some conster-
nation among those present.

The theme of the convention had been grassland farming
and conservation. Alfred returned home with a wealth of information and filled with enthusiasm; sure that he was right in
planning his grassland programme.

When Daisy arrived the following day, she became,
whether she wished it or not, the polite listener to detailed
plans for grassland farming, and all the benefits it would bring
through the years. We felt vaguely sorry for her, exposed to all
this enthusiasm that could not be subdued. We made up for it
as best we could with cutter rides, homemade bread, fresh eggs
and sunshine.

We were not sorry that the programme had been started
with the crop of rye. Reading and thinking produced an idea
that would cover all our fields, leaving nothing bare the following winter. Sweet clover! Why not sow it with the grain in each
field that was not being seeded down till the following year?
The more he thought of the idea, the better Alfred liked it, and
could find no reason why it would not be entirely satisfactory.

We had borrowed from the bank all our statement from a
safe investment angle would permit, and had loans to repay.
The one for the roof on the house was the hardest to pay back,
but we cleared it off, as was our habit.

Just before Christmas that year, Alfred went in to the bank
with a number of cheques, proceeds from poultry, pigs, cattle,
the gravel pit, and a pension cheque. It came to something over
a thousand dollars, and we had notes to pay.

"I'd like it all in cash please," Alfred told the teller, who
obediently counted it out. I was in the butcher shop buying suet
for Christmas mincemeat when Alfred came in.

"Here, don't ever say I didn't give you anything." He
pressed a wad of bills into my hands. "Count it."

I counted it, I'd never held so much money in my hands
before. Our friend the butcher stood by watching, incredulous.
What were we up to now? I handed it back to Alfred, glowing
with pride, because we'd earned it by hard work. He said, "I
thought you deserved the privilege of holding it, if only for a few
minutes before I go back and pay off our notes."

We all laughed, and Alfred returned to the bank, giving the wondering teller no reason at all for his strange actions as he paid it all back on our various notes. We'd start the New Year as we always had, and hoped we always would, with a clean sheet, even if on the second of January Alfred borrowed it all back again. We had fun. The money came, slipped through our fingers and went. "The Doings" could not have been a fitter name for it.

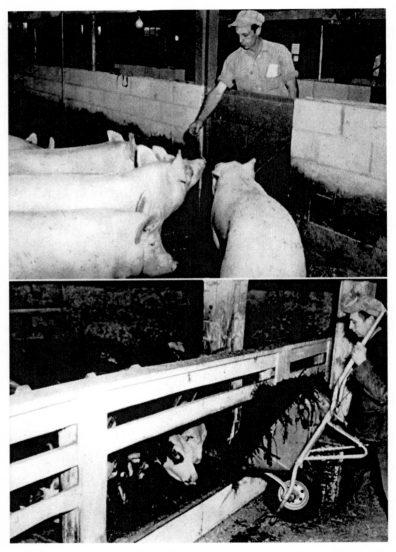

Top: Purebred English Yorkshire sows, the nucleus of a breeding herd on Friendship Farm.

Bottom: Dumping grass silage into the manger.

Top: Alfred Leatherbarrow chatting with Junior Farmers.

Bottom: Group of Junior Farmers listening to talk by Alfred
Leatherbarrow prior to a tour of Friendship Farm.

.

CHAPTER 10

"I'd like to talk to Dr. Weir about the sweet clover idea," Alfred announced one day.

"Then, let's go down to the College," I said.

It's as easy as that. You have an idea or a problem, and you take it to the Department at the College specializing in whatever branch of agriculture your particular problem is associated with. We lived just seventeen miles away, so preferred a personal contact to correspondence.

Dishes stacked, I hurriedly gather up my knitting, reading and writing materials, and we are off like two adventurers. There was no need for Alfred to be concerned about my comfort out in the car, with my reading and knitting, and the people who passed by to watch.

Alfred talked for several hours about his ideas and what he planned to do, coming out to tell me all they had had to say about everything as we drove home.

"What does he think of the sweet clover idea?"

"Thinks it's fine."

Dr. Weir had said, "Go ahead and let me know how it turns out."

Reassured by all he'd read, heard and thought about throughout the winter, and an interested "Go ahead" from the College, Alfred ordered his grass seed from a local merchant. We had sat up nights figuring out how, without any extra operation, Alfred could put a cover crop on fields he was sowing to grain with the idea of seeding them down the following year. It was through this thinking that Alfred hit on the sweet clover idea. At that time, the extra cost would be approximately 75 cents an acre for sweet clover seeds without any extra field operation. This would provide a cover crop, fall pasture, two-and-a-half tons of roots per acre for organic matter in the soil, and help inoculate the soil for legumes that had not been in this soil for a good ten years.

Alfred called the merchant in the morning to see if he had any sweet clover seed.

"Yes, I have some of last year's. It was cheaper then, and I'll give it to you for that price, just to get rid of it."

"How much have you?"

"Three bushels."

"I'll take it all."

From then till seeding time the grass and legume seed for our new venture stood as before with its mouse trap on guard behind the living-room door. "Our treasure." Going up and down the cellar stairs as I did before and after every meal to keep food cool, I would look at the bags and contemplate the future with a feeling of wonder and excitement that from then on has never left me. We had all our eggs in one basket, so to speak—The Soil.

It was so much more now than just a way of life, or making a living. We were being instrumental in bringing new life to worn-out land. Like a scientist working to isolate a germ, we worked to bring new life to soil abandoned as run-out, dead.

The spring work commenced. With nostalgic pleasure, I went to the barn to help clean the grain, and look again through the granary window up over the hill with its patches of snow on the black earth—black, because it was wet and bare, never to be this way again.

Moving barn furniture in readiness for the time it would be needed, watching Alfred work on the seeder and helping him paint the one-way disc, seeing how well he'd gauged his supply and demand that winter, knowing what stock we had had been well and amply fed, seeing little more than enough hay left in the mows to look after the horses when they had to be kept in the stable to be handy for work during the spring and summer after the cattle went out to pasture—it filled me with pride. He was an excellent manager, wasting nothing, always having something coming in from somewhere to swell "The Doings" when the need arose.

That we chose not to buy meat for a few months in order to purchase more fertilizer was a free and willing gesture on our part towards insuring greater abundance in the years to come, and thereafter no scarcity of meat.

I well remember once during our self-imposed vegetarian diet, going in to Perry's on a Sunday afternoon and finding Blanche cooking a delicious smelling roast of beef. It made me ravenous. Ordinarily they would have invited us to stay to dinner and that day we would have accepted with alacrity. Perry apologized.

"We're having a couple in for dinner and the roast isn't very big."

"Oh, we couldn't stay anyway, thanks," and with drooling mouths, we got out. The safest place for us was home. We went there.

The exquisite luxury of sitting at his work and the speed with which it could be accomplished protected Alfred against physical exhaustion, but did nothing to stop the treadmill of worry he travelled constantly. Telling him not to worry, reassuring him in every possible way, was of no avail.

"I'm a born worrier, and if I haven't something to worry about, I'll make it," he would say.

Sometimes he'd be irritable. That would make me the same until we would realize that we were making each other miserable. Then an effort would be made to stop it, and Alfred would tell me something of what was bothering him. Bringing it out in the open always helped. You could see it, then, for the poor thing it was, and feel disgust at letting it interfere with our happiness. Alfred went doggedly on with his purpose, sowing the sweet clover seed on the land he did not seed down with a grass legume mixture. Also adding some of the sweet clover, as an extra, to the seed mixture for the other fields, thus using all he'd bought.

"Well, it's done now. We'll see if I'm right."

We didn't say anything about the possibility it would be wrong, for trying an experiment like this means a year and more gained or lost. It is a long period of time to gamble on when you haven't much of this world's goods to do it with, or any encouragement from those around you who have farmed all their lives.

It was all right for Dr. Weir to say, "Go ahead, and let me know how it turns out." He wouldn't suffer one way or the other. Nor would the theorists or wealthy experimenters who could easily afford a gamble. No wonder Alfred worried until he had pains continuously in his stomach, with all the symptoms of ulcers, except hemorrhages. From his stomach the pain would go to his chest, and everyone would say, "You are too thin, Alfred."

I thought he must have a tape worm, for he ate well, good nourishing food, looking all the while like starvation in the midst of plenty. It worried me. His disease was worry; the cure, a successful experiment; and we had to wait the results of that for a year and more, alone.

The last on the road to buy a tractor, Alfred was the first to buy a one-way disc to replace the plow, which we sold at the first opportunity.

Now it was time to work on the mangel ground. This, according to plan, was to be the last year we would have a root crop. In discussion with farmers there was much controversy about the relative merits of turnips and mangels. Most considered the turnips superior in nutrient value, so Alfred determined to find out the difference in them, if any. He asked the Agricultural Representative for figures on this, and learned that mangels were better than turnips. In our experience they were also a more certain crop, with higher tonnage to the acre. We planned on sowing mangels on two acres at the front, and Alfred proceeded to fit it for the seed.

Remembering what he'd heard about the leaching of manure, Alfred drew the manure direct from a loafing barn to the field, which also meant only one handling; spread as much as he considered he could cut in the same day with the one way disc, usually spreading till four p.m.; then discing till all was mixed in.

A neighbour inquired about what he was doing and, being told, replied,

"Oh, you're all wrong, man. Everybody plows for mangels."

"I don't want to bury it," Alfred told him. "I want to mix it in with my open bottom soil. Everything buried keeps on going down. I doubt if the roots could ever catch up with it."

The older man shook his head and walked away, no doubt feeling sorry for his neighbour.

Alfred then sowed the recommended fertilizer, with half a strip being salted as well to see if it made any difference. It did increase tonnage about fifteen per cent. It was cultivated once, and our expert plowman friend rowed it up for us, we following a few rows behind, Alfred guiding the seeder and I leading the horse, with vicious thoughts each time our feet got tangled. No doubt a lot of unnecessary pity was wasted on us that day also, for to our friend this method was all wrong.

The mangels appeared in five days, and one week later we started the laborious task of thinning, with practically no transplanting to do. The mangels next to the road could be watched, and were, and one neighbour told Alfred they were the best crop he had ever seen. They were tremendous. From the two acres we completely filled the root cellar, which was fifty-five feet long, 10 feet wide and 10 feet high. We fed mangels daily to all the stocks—twenty-three head of cattle, seventy odd pigs and 500 chickens—till the following May. We are told mangels are ninety per cent water. We think it must be awfully good water; at least the stock enjoyed it. Very often one mangel would fill a two-gallon pail. So Alfred's experiment with mangel ground was successful. There was better germination, and very little transplanting. The fact that Alfred's method was proven right did not change the mind of our friend who had watched and criticized. He never varied from the old method, or grew very good mangels.

The spring of 1950 was very wet, and it continued so right on through to haying time. At such times the silent submissive fanner can only stand still, his mind numb, waiting, waiting. Each day increases his anxiety as the lush crop grows to maturity. The thick rich green is gradually veiled in shades from white on through lavender to deepest purple, as the alfalfa and clovers ripen and blossom, till finally they pass that moment when the good farmer should cut it down for curing. Ten per cent in blossom is believed to be the time when it is at saturation point for protein. Some farmers, anxious to get a little more bulk, wait; but that is because they do not know. No farmer wants anything but the best. With the weather so uncertain, what will he do? Last year he stood on the same knoll and watched the storm clouds gather, promising life to his parched fields. They were so thick that the sun was obliterated, and a dark hush seemed the prelude to a storm. Then, as though a giant hand had suddenly scooped the storm clouds up, they disappear, and the sun pours down from a hot blue sky to blister the grain and grasses. Dejected, hopeless, the farmer plods to the cool, empty solace of his barn, where he can't see the desolation being wrought on this year's harvest.

What a contrast, what a tragedy! No wonder the farmer, through the years, too often with so little education, has become suspicious of anything coming from books. He reads the farm magazines, but does not absorb their information, his usual comment, "Sounds all right, but I'll go on the way my father did." He is afraid, afraid to take a chance, for what he is doing now is uncertain enough.

"I don't know why I can't make any more," he says, "I work hard."

So he does, from dawn till long past dusk, and goes to church every Sunday. He's so superstitious he's afraid not to. He talks to his neighbour about the weather, and has got into the habit of always finding fault with it. It's too dry, or too wet, or too hot. In fact, he almost wills the worst to happen, perhaps that he may then indulge in self-pity and blame his inability to make much money on everything but himself. The Government is a big bully; he's safe in blaming everything on it. With the reason for his failure securely placed where it belongs, he can swagger a little and be secretive about just what he makes, for that's his business, and besides it's little enough compared to the income of those capitalists.

I wonder how many tread this treadmill, and refuse to make use of the wealth of practical assistance so readily available. I understand it is generally felt by our agricultural scientists that it takes ten years to get the average farmer to change his methods.

I firmly believe that the power is in us under any circumstances, in any climate where man can live, to improve our methods according to the nature of the land so that it will produce food and maintain life. For centuries everything has been taken out; now it is time to give back if we want to live. I can give no better example of how much more the soil returns to us, once its needs are considered, than this our own story.

It rained.   The poor weatherman must have felt sorry for the farmers listening hopefully for a favourable report. We hung on his words, and having learned that his report was so nearly accurate, acted always upon it. Stretching the haying season over into harvest time, we sacrificed protein saturation point to have dry, well-cured hay, and succeeded in getting into the mows all but one small piece in good condition. This had been cut, but was a heavy crop, thanks to the manure that had been cultivated in just prior to seeding. "All wrong," quoth a neighbour whose new seed was no good at all. The hay not quite dry enough to take in on Saturday. We didn't like to be too contrary, and the custom is never to do field work on Sunday; so, hopefully, it was left till Monday. Monday came, but the rain had come on Sunday night.

"I'm not going to be so dependent on weather again" Alfred said. "Let's go see if we can find out something about silos for grass silage."

We started out. Perry was building a block silo for a farmer near Fergus. We went there first. It looked nice but the cost wasn't, and Alfred was curious about trench silos. He had tried to persuade a neighbour to dig one the previous year; working together with the equipment they had would have suited both financially. Alone, we hadn't the money to do it. The neighbour wasn't interested beyond discussing it. Having read a lot about them Alfred had had plenty of information for him, but to no avail.

With an idea of the possible cost of silos, we decided to first find out what equipment we would need. We travelled the countryside every rainy day, visiting farmers where Alfred knew of or saw forage equipment being used. Each farmer, helpful always, would direct us to other farms where different types were in use. The problem that presented itself to us with a conventional forage harvester was the amount of equipment involved. It meant three tractors, and three forage wagons, one at the barn unloading, one going back and forth to the field and one in the field being loaded. As well as a forage harvester, a blower for unloading was needed. This would entail working in with other farmers which Alfred didn't want to do because in a short period he would lose the cost of the equipment in lost protein. There is only one time to cut a crop of grass and legumes that is at protein saturation point. This is important not only from an economic angle but, even more so from the standpoint of plant health.

It seemed to be an insurmountable problem, till one farmer told Alfred of McKee Brothers in Elmira. A pair of ingenious twins with exploratory minds were working with a collection of pipes and fan trying to invent a one-man forage harvester for hay and straw.

It was still early in the afternoon, so we wended our way to Elmira, and located the undersized workshop and one of the twins.

"I hear you are making a forage harvester. Do you mind showing it to me?"

"Sure. That's it over there. We are working on it. It's just a model. We are developing it to pick up dry hay and straw."

"How will it work on grass silage?"

"Hadn't thought of that."

"You'd better. It's the coming thing."

"There would have to be a lot more work done on it; besides, we've no place to try it."

"Well, I have some grass that's just in the right state to try out."

"Where do you live?"

"Eleven miles from here."

Their mother, a widow, who did the office work, was startled when Gerald announced, "I'm loading the machine on the truck and going over to Elora to try it on green grass."

"Oh! Should you?" she replied. He followed us home.

For the rest of the afternoon, until almost dark, the three men worked to iron out the wrinkles, and figure out how the new machine in the inventive stage could be made to work.

"You can put me down for your first machine next spring," Alfred said. He was confident that this brain child of the McKee Brothers would serve our requirements. Not only was it half the price of the conventional harvester and blower, as it did both jobs of loading and unloading, but it meant getting away from a lot of extra equipment and the need to work in with a group of farmers. It was a one-man harvester, needing only one tractor, one wagon and one man to operate.

Several neighbours, watching it work the following year, said farmers had been waiting fifty years for such a machine. Today, this machine is being sold all over Canada and the United States.

"Well," Alfred said quite happily that night before we went to bed, "I have just saved half of what I thought it was going to cost me to get into forage harvesting equipment. If it's still raining tomorrow, we'll visit the places we heard had different types of silos. I don't care if it costs me every animal on the farm, I'm going to put my crop in as grass silage next year and not have to combat the weather."

The following day it rained. We didn't sit in the house or hide in the barn or gossip at the corner store. We went looking for silos, every kind, cement tower, block, octagonal, trench. We found only two trench silos. One was an old foundation of a root cellar in a barn that had been burnt down. The farmer was using this for corn silage. The other was in a gravel pit where they had put up stakes and boarded up on the inside and back-filled. The grass was put in long. This farmer was an Englishman and he gave Alfred some interesting literature on grass silage and its storage in England.

After two weeks of intensive reading and studying and discussion with his friend, Dr. Weir, at the College, Alfred definitely decided on a trench silo and where he would put it. It would be one that would hold around 275 tons of silage and situated so that the silage would be handled only once in filling and once in feeding. The trench silo was decided upon for this reason. Other types of silo big enough to hold that much grass would entail the building of two uprights, costing $1,000 each; a lot of money to us. The trench silo, dug by Alfred, formed by a carpenter, and cement poured by a contractor cost only $310.

"Hurrah!" said Alfred, "I can still have my harvester and silo and not sell any of my cattle." How tremendously this sparked our enthusiasm it would be impossible to convey.

Grass silage stored in an upright silo means a lot of work getting it in, and a lot more getting it out and in front of the animals. The disadvantage of a tower silo for grass is its height, as the great depth of silage thirty to forty feet, compresses the bottom half so much that a lot of the juice (which is protein) is squeezed out and lost. It has not had the proper amount of air retained to cause a good fermentation, so the silage is more stinking and sour and, therefore, not as palatable. You also have frost on the sides. A trench silo is easier to fill. In our case, the silage is below the level of the ground and is much easier to take out; no danger of frost on the sides, and having a depth of only ten feet will not have the same pressure to squeeze out the juice. The level being brought up more slowly in filling, it retains a sufficient quantity of air to cause a better fermentation and sweeter-smelling and more palatable silage.

With the new harvester equipment and silo costing so much less than we had thought possible, we settled down to our game of tag with the weather, which was so unsettled and unseasonable that year. Because we knew what we were about we were less dejected by the thwarting elements; enjoying our rainy days with long hours to plan the future.

CHAPTER 11

Near the centre of a fifteen-acre field, with rolling slopes that
started from the highest level on the farm and gradually
descended from bare knoll to bare knoll to almost the lowest
level, was a plot about one-third the size of the field. It could be
called a waterway in spring, particularly if our next door neighbour had left the adjoining field bare all winter. Little gullies
wended their circuitous way around the knolls to the low land;
here a veritable flood carried the top soil from the heights
across the field, depositing a little of the rich soil, as it continued on to spend itself on the low field on the other side of the
lane. This field was green now, with twitch grass that we hadn't
killed as we had hoped to do the year we cultivated with a four-
horse team sixteen times.

Alfred prepared to attack, waving gaily to me as he passed
the house shouting, "Here goes for the blitz on twitch."

He one-way disced the field three times at intervals, as it
appeared green, following the final discing immediately (the
next day) with the seed he planted to use as green manure.
Buckwheat on ten acres, oats on three; and because we had no
more seed to spare for this operation, we decided it was as good
a time as any to see just how successful open summer fallow
really was, on two acres.

We were fast developing a young experimental farm. Not
content with just reading about new methods, Alfred liked to
try them out for himself, and I delighted to see him do it. The
added interest it stimulated was good for our morale. Alfred
also found that to have an alternative plan in readiness in case
the original wasn't developing as it should, was to stand him in
good stead later in the summer.

When the buckwheat and oats were up anywhere from two
to three feet, he one-way disced it all, left it for three weeks, cul-

tivated it once, and the following day sowed wheat with 250 lbs. of recommended fertilizer to the acre.

"Man, you aren't going to sacrifice that nice crop of buckwheat, are you?" a neighbour asked.

"Yes. This field has produced nothing since I came here. Now I'm going to build it up so it will."

Alfred's bedside table is always stacked with reading material. Here, burning the midnight oil can be taken literally, and many times he put the reading away because the lamp burned dry, particularly if I'd manoeuvred it to do so. One night the reading continued until about two a.m. No doubt my restless tossing interfered with his concentration on some very interesting nutrient tables he'd received from O.A.C.

Then he began figuring out the nutrient value of his various crops, and soon found the results so interesting he had to get up and work it out accurately on paper. Sitting in the kitchen at four a.m. with a pot of coffee, reading over what his figuring had arrived at, he contemplated the future for this farm, and it was rosy indeed. A crop of grain running eighty bushels to the acre (and few farms around here today average as much as that) produces three hundred pounds of available nutrient at a cost of $18.50 per acre, which includes all operations in fitting, seeding and fertilizer, from the time the grain leaves the granary till it is back again.

Compare this with a grass legume mixture, putting the first cutting into a silo and using the second as dry hay or pasture, at a cost of $9.50 per acre. With far less work attached, or climatic hazard, it would produce upwards of 1,500 lbs. of available nutrient per acre. Not even a dry spring would affect a crop taken the latter part of May or early in June as grass silage, and it could be ensiled in any kind of weather providing one wanted to work in it. Fertility improves rapidly when the soil is seeded to grass and legumes. In fact it can't be built up in any better or cheaper way than under sod. So, we couldn't afford to grow grain.

The added encouragement this gave us to carry through a difficult summer to an autumn when our new methods would be noticed and commented on, stood us in good stead. Waiting a year for proof that a decision is right is hard enough for anyone. For us, with nothing but advice and criticism, no backlog of capital, and heavy expenditures on equipment to be made, it was a wild gamble, all or nothing. Telling me all his theories, arrived at through observation, reading and talking, Alfred would not underestimate the risk we were taking but rather enlarge upon it so that I would be prepared if it proved to be a grim failure. The possibilities sounded exciting and wonderful. We were filled with that same delicious sense of well-being that one has when secretly performing a charitable act that will not bring recognition. An exaltation carried us through the difficult time. Our grain crop was the best we'd ever had, and better than the farm had known. We were going out of grain as a crop to be harvested—in a blaze of glory.

The front field was cut and stooked. I drove the tractor. Alfred rode the binder. It was lovely, slicing down the golden grain in the warm summer sun, startling the snakes and field mice, leaving uncovered the pesky woodchuck holes so neatly hidden in the tall grain. As a team, we did well together. Alfred stooked it all, and then proceeded to give me my first lesson on building a load of grain.

How you start is all important—building a good heart to anchor the slippery sheaves. Alfred placed all the sheaves, simply by throwing them in correctly, heads to me, butts away. As the load grew, I'd indicate the area with my fork where I wanted the sheaf, and he'd toss it to the very spot. I had very little arranging to do, and that only as the load grew and Alfred couldn't see where a sheaf was needed.

"This is easy," I shouted to a gratified husband, who wanted my work to be as light as possible.

Wherever there was new seed, Alfred wanted to put the grain in the barn, in case the threshing machine was long delayed on other farms. The uncertain weather had continued right on from hay time to harvest, and everything had been delayed. We had half the grain from the front field in the barn, and were up on the "top of the world" binding its first good crop. The topography was anything but level, with a steep slope the length of the field. Alfred had trouble keeping the canvases tight enough. Giving one an extra vicious tug, something in his forearm snapped and it became so painful he had to go to the doctor. It proved to be a torn ligament. With his arm in a cast, and having to go somewhere till it dried sufficiently before driving home, Alfred went to my brother Matt's, with the idea also of finding out if he knew anyone who could work for us until Alfred could use his arm again. A man was located, but he couldn't come for a couple of days. Matt, on holidays, offered to come out the following day. We were too grateful to be kind and "refuse."

The binder had given up on the steepest slope, and Alfred had to ask a neighbour if he would finish binding the rest of the field and do the back one also. In emergencies, particularly when a crop is in danger of being lost, there is no man more willing, considerate or ready with a plan that will take care of the crop. He was almost finished with his own, and would come right over and do ours. In return, Alfred would do some one-way discing in the fall for him. The emergency, we thought, was taken care of.

Matt arrived in the morning to help Alfred stook. After an early dinner, like warriors we proceeded to the battleground, only Alfred knowing the hardship ahead for two greenhorns. Helpless to make anything easier for us, he drove the tractor and watched.

Willy-nilly, heads or butts, the sheaves came flying to me; I danced like a dervish, up and down the load, determined to place each sheaf as I'd been taught, and build a heart that would ensure no load slipping off. I wouldn't dare catch Alfred's eye as he gazed helplessly up at me, for I could see the perspiration pouring off my brother's beet red face, his tired eyes smiling into mine as we assured the other everything was going fine, silently determined to clear the field that day.

The final torment for me was dragging my aching body round the kitchen as I prepared a meal. I was too tired to eat, while Matt suffered in grim determination his final ordeal of the day.

The dairy herd had been gradually cut till we had one cow, and her nursing. This cow we tethered in the pasture near the house for obvious practical reasons, and the calf far enough off that we might milk the cow once a day for our own supply. The calf was getting big and strong and, with this great expanse of pasture, objected to being tethered. It had been a battle for some time now, and the calf had lost with an ever slimmer margin each day. Matt offered to handle the calf, and the moment the rope was untied from the post, it was off, heels in the air racing every which way, but slyly out of reach of any post. Matt hung on, finally sitting on the ground. It all happened so quickly,

"Let go," we shouted.

He either didn't hear or wouldn't be beaten by a calf, for it dragged him over rocks and twigs and cow manure indiscriminately and still he hung on, winning at last.

Coming in for supper, I saw his hands, blistered from unaccustomed handling of a hay fork. Now they were broken and bleeding and still my brother grinned.

"Oh, it's nothing," Matt protested. "It's nothing, honestly," and he was off to attend a lacrosse game it would be sacrilege to miss.

We used slings to unload at the barn. That was one time and labour-saving device at least which Alfred had been smart enough to acquire at a sale. Alfred was to call for our man in Fergus every morning, and return at night—a bother, but we were lucky to get someone at this time for such a short period.

Alfred started for the car in the morning as I, milk-pail in hand, started out to the pasture to milk the cow. I sat on an upturned pail facing the lane, to watch Alfred pass. The sweetness of dew, wet clover and warm milk tickled my nostrils as looking up, I saw the faint pink tinge of morning appear behind the lifting mist, and Alfred giving me the high hat as he passed, looking for all the world like a man with time on his hands and no cares. We would laugh at the picture we made. Maw at the milking. Paw, the dandy, off to town. I was lucky, we only had one cow. Twenty-three young steers were the total of our beef programme just nicely started. It wasn't long before, with pencil and paper and the recollection of struggles with the calf, carrying water, and changing the tether, Alfred decided the first good offer for the cow would take us out of dairy work entirely. We could feed a steer with less work and no extra cost, and make more money buying powdered and condensed milk by the case for the house.

The man who offered to work in our emergency, past his prime, was not too good at stooking, even with Alfred helping him, and he broke the cast three times doing things he shouldn't, before it came off for good. Finally, the older man's young son took his place in time to help at the first threshing Alfred would have to go to, or supply a man, in order to have his own done.

Our neighbour came over with his binder to finish the cutting with Alfred, a one-armed driver on the tractor. After making a round each way to open the field, he remarked, "My goodness, that's a good crop."

After six more rounds, he had to stop again to make a minor adjustment, and as he stood there looking over the field of tall, waving grain, he remarked, "I shouldn't say it, Alf, but that's the best crop I've ever cut. What I can't understand is that anyone with grain anywhere near that height finds that it is laying flat this year because of the storms we've had. Yet yours is standing as straight as can be all over the field. How do you account for it?"

"Just a little experiment I tried this year. I knew the field was in good heart, and that I would most likely get a good crop off it, so I added extra potash when I was sowing it."

"What will that do?"

"Potash helps make a stronger stalk, and this certainly proves it."

"Oh, I don't think that will make any difference," he said— in spite of the fact that the evidence given was so apparent.

The grain stood about four and a half feet all over the field, running about eighty bushels to the acre. So they continued to finish cutting the field, Alfred resting the arm with the cast on the mudguard of the tall tractor enjoying the sensation of feeling the heads of the tall grain hit his fingers constantly as he drove along, listening to the continuous "click, click, click" of the knotter as the heavy crop kept it running like a clock. A rich reward, he felt this was, for all the time, work and thought he'd given this field; a fitting climax to the growing of grain on this farm. Like the mangels it was unsurpassed.

That was a big field to stook single-handed, which Alfred set out to do while the boy took his place at the threshing. I helped him in the afternoons. Only the realization that we had nothing to complain about kept us doggedly at it, and thankful for this good crop. The plan was to stook thresh this field, hauling all the rest to the barn because it was standing on new seed, and if left very long would not only kill the seed but no doubt suffer itself as well.

Between threshings, the boy worked on our own farm where we found his scant experience was costing us more than it was worth to keep the work up-to-date. The horses, for the first time in our experience, ran away. Fortunately, the boy was not hurt, but the repairs cost us money we had pigeonholed for other things. There was never any surplus set aside for emergencies as anything we had to spend money on was an emergency. So, with a partial cast, Alfred felt he could manage, and we were gloriously alone again. It rained and rained. Threshing was held up, as all the farmers were stook threshing and none but us thought of putting the grain in the barn whenever possible. We kept right at it as long as Alfred didn't have to be away. If there was any grain dry, we put it in the barn. Using the team now and slings, we started to clear the back field. It was wonderful driving down over the slope, looking at the stocks so big and close together, a crop to be proud of, and we were justly proud. Day after day, we worked under a blistering hot sun. It took us a week, and that week proved to be the only week of dry weather we had. Alfred's threshing gang were at work on farms where he was not required to help, making it possible to keep at our own.

"It will be such a long time before they get to our farm with this uncertain weather," he said, "I think it wisest to put all we can in the barn, then we'll know it's safe."

On every farm, fields with stocked grain, ripe and golden, waited for the threshers. After that one dry week, it rained every two or three days, week after week. Stook threshers despaired. They had waited. Having planned their harvest that way, that way it had to be done. Fatalistically, martyrs to their vocation, they sacrificed grain that sprouted in the stocks, turned black and killed the new seed where it stood.

"They wouldn't think of putting the grain in their barns," said Alfred. "There is nothing as stubborn as a weather-beaten farmer. He'd defy the Almighty."

What wasn't lost in the field, was later lost through heating in the granaries. A bounteous crop destroyed by man's stubborn determination to do a job one way and one way only.

Having an alternative plan and following it through filled our granary; for the first time it was full of ripe, hard golden grain. We hadn't had to worry about a thing not even fall plowing held up by the late season for we weren't going to plow any more.

Talking the new methods over with farmers was very frustrating. They had no comments, no ideas, no suggestions. Only one spoke up in all sincerity, because he was a friend and didn't want to see Alfred go broke.

"Why, look man," he said, as they stood on the brow of a hill looking over the countryside, "Why are all those fields black? Everybody plows in the fall. They can't all be wrong."

For him, the majority ruled. For us, we blazed our own trail, were laughed at, and providing food for a good large part of the talk at any gossip session we weren't present at, which was most of them.

When the snow came, we couldn't change our minds. On the surface all was calm, but Alfred silently rode his merry-go-round of worry.

Nevertheless, we paid the taxes, notes and interest on time, with pig cheques, gravel cheques, a few dollars and the proceeds from half a dozen culls. December always found "The Doings" at low ebb, but come January, money seemed to roil in from everywhere, and our optimism never waned.

We had a glorious Christmas. Daisy came up to celebrate it with us and, planning to return later for a longer winter holiday, left her red flannel pyjamas, snow suit and mitts behind. We were jinxed on Christmas Day, as usual. Later we saw the movie Daisy took as I drove the tractor pulling the car Alfred tried vainly to get going. After I ditched the tractor, we gave up and the family came out in a taxi.

We decided the kitchen had to be painted, and the winter was our time for such jobs. White, this time, with red trim. The table and chairs a blue, which Alfred mixed to match the blue of the Old Willow dishes that made such an attractive display in our open cupboards.

"Let's paint the back of the cupboards red too," I said.

"No."

"Yes."

I saw I had to prove it would look nice. With no Christmas red wrapping paper left, what was there large enough to get the effect? Daisy's red flannel pyjamas, of course. So for several days Daisy's pyjamas formed a backdrop for my Willow cups hanging from hooks in the shelves above. I won my point; but in my excitement I used an outdoor regal red instead of the enamel we'd bought for the kitchen. It took ages to dry. I'd even argued with Alfred that I had the right paint.

Later, when the warm weather came, I wanted to paint the front and back doors red, but received a flat "No" from my spouse. He was away one day, and I got the back door painted red. I know he liked it, but the front is still white. Perhaps he's right.

January found Alfred back in Toronto at the Soil and Crop Improvement Convention, again choosing his day carefully to hear the speakers he most wanted to and returning home late at night, his eyes shining with enthusiasm.

"I just heard a lecture on the Rain Drop by Dr. Harrold, of the U.S. Hydrological Station, Cochocton, Ohio. He spoke for an hour and a half and didn't waste a word, and when he was finished I watched his exit and followed, knowing he couldn't get away before I reached him. We talked for another hour. I told him what I was doing in the front field with sweet clover. He was so interested he wrote it all down and said he was sure it would work the way we expect it to. I told him how everybody in the district thought I was crazy and he said, 'Don't worry. In a few years they'll all be following you, or wishing they were. You are just several jumps ahead. They will be forced into it themselves some day.'"

After this meeting with Dr. Harrold, Alfred's tensions were so relieved that spring just couldn't come soon enough. Here he had the best authority to back up his ideas.

"As long as a few men like him think I'm right, I don't care what anybody else thinks."

What Alfred heard that day substantiated all he'd done in the fields, and dissolved the last of his lingering doubts. With the confidence of knowing he was right, Alfred signed the contract, presented one stormy winter day by a little man in a bowler hat, for delivery of a McKee Pneumatic Harvester in the spring. He took the 10.20 tractor to our friendly garage and had it checked over and a power take-off put on. We were all set for spring, riding high and happy. We even decided electricity could be managed, and made a special trip to Elmira for the sole purpose of signing up for it.

The evening after our trip to Elmira was spent playing our favourite game, bridge, with friends in town, a garage-owner and his wife, who took care of all Alfred's repairs and had put the power take-off on the old 10.20 in readiness for harvesting the grass silage. As we sat around our friend's dining-room table, drinking coffee and eating delicious sandwiches, the conversation between the two men drifted to bathrooms and the plumbing required in the country. I had often remarked that I'd rather have a bathroom than electricity, if I had to choose. As the men talked, one difficulty after another was overcome, until we were quite keyed up and excited over the prospect of having both electricity and a bathroom. We talked till 3 a.m.

We drove home through a blustering snowstorm, Alfred's mind occupied with pipes and bolts, sewage disposal and pressure pumps, mine toying with colour schemes, painting the bathroom and getting out towels to flatter my choice of colour. Suddenly I looked out.

"We've gone past our road," I shouted.

Sure enough we had. We had both been so busy installing and decorating a bathroom that we didn't know where we were.

CHAPTER 12

The farm wife's spending money! We opened a separate account at the bank, in my name, for all the money we received as wedding gifts. There were so many things we wanted and more we needed that we were too confused about how best it could be spent to spend any immediately.

On the numerous days when I found myself alone, with Alfred away at a sale or helping a neighbour, I'd look with a critical eye at the house, room after room, and visualize the homey comfort we longed to realize. In a warm April sun, the promise of spring blooming fresh and sweet all around us, it was easy to see sparkling clean sunny rooms with frilly curtains, reflecting our happiness. But I couldn't figure out what to spend the money on first.

When Alfred came home with some money he'd earned helping a neighbour, I snapped out of the spending dream and started to think of what a good farm wife should be doing to help her husband in his business. Chickens, of course! I recoiled from the thought and hoped I had hidden my distaste when we talked about it.

Alfred wasn't thinking much about chickens either, but they would produce eggs for our own use and perhaps pay for the groceries. He didn't urge me. We toyed with the idea and I talked myself into an enthusiasm I almost felt and wouldn't back out of.

Neither of us realized what a good paying proposition poultry was till some time later, so the first fifty started chicks were bought with not too much thought regarding their true worth in farm economics. After they arrived and had to be fed and watered, my humanitarian instincts compelled me to be interested in their proper feeding, and I quite naturally sought information on feeding from a farmer's wife who was engaged in caring for a large flock. The rebuff, perhaps, I should have expected. After all, a good business man does not tell his secrets to a competitor. Why should I be given information that would enable me to go into the poultry business in a big way and perhaps influence the lowering of prices by over-production?

The secretiveness borne of greed, a common trait of man all through our civilization, keeps us grovelling like the miserable creatures our greed has made us become. We war with one another, be it the individual or the entire race, having lost faith to such an extent we can't trust one another any more. In church we pray for blessings individually. In our homes we seek the comforts we desire with no care for the individual or community good. We will take ever by force, yet give nothing.

So my rebuff was not necessarily personal, but rather typical of our times. Alfred and I talked about it, and we decided if in the course of our life on the farm we were asked information that would help our fellowman, we would give it. Life was too short to be shrivelled by selfish secretiveness if good fortune blessed our work.

I got out all the books and pamphlets on poultry. I was as concerned over their health and welfare as I would be with an ailing child and it my own. We laugh now at the memory of my herding the tiny feathered creatures in and out of their house each day when they would much prefer to decide for themselves whether they would go out or stay in, and were better able to. They grew, and in due course I proudly collected the first eggs, thinking I had performed a miracle. I must have been very annoying to these industrious birds. Once they started to lay, I buzzed in and out so frequently, and disturbed them so much that their production probably wasn't as good as it would have been had they been left peacefully alone.

Alfred got too much pleasure out of watching my enjoyment to say anything. One day, some of my family were out, and asked if I had any eggs to sell. I thought I could spare a dozen, but found we were short one egg. It was getting late in the afternoon and I didn't know chickens work just so many hours a day, like any sensible man. Very businesslike, I hurried to the barn to see if there were any more eggs, while Alfred and our guests sat on the back step watching me, filled with importance in the little industry that was mine to watch over. I returned dejected; my chickens had let me down. There were no more eggs that day.

In the spring of 1947, we purchased 500 day-old mixed chicks. Having bought a brooder stove and all the necessary little troughs and water bottles, we fixed up the garage, building a room inside it that could easily be opened at one end if it would be needed for a car.

The day the chicks arrived, we sat on a bag of feed in a corner and watched them scurrying hither and thither, bumping into each other, picking at everything and filling our ears with the din of their chirping. This was my first lot of day-old chicks, and I was nervous, excited and delighted with my job. We put newspapers down daily for the first ten days; then, as they started picking the paper to pieces too fast, one day we rolled it all up to burn and put in straw. At first the chicks were terrified, crowding together and making us fear they would suffocate. Next time I was more careful of my nervous charges when changing the appointments of their living quarters. Chickens like things to be left the way they've always known them, just like father and his slippers and pipe and newspaper. I soon learned the value of "Please do not disturb" in production.

As you watch the chickens on range, you may not notice the hawk that has appeared in the sky until you see heads lift and feel a stillness that lasts a split second; then every chicken speeds to shelter, and the circling hawk has to settle for a field mouse, if it's lucky.

In less than a month, twenty-four of my carefully tended baby chicks had succumbed to avian coccidiosis. All the literature so carefully read made my problem of evading the disease seem so tremendous that I despaired of ever being able to eliminate it. Also, losing so many birds in such a short time made profit on the enterprise look pretty slim. Treatment before we lost the chicks was going to be worth looking into another year. However, selling the cockerels in the summer paid for the chicks and their feed to date, and soon they would be laying, paying their own way and finally bringing us a profit. It was quite a job moving the pullets from the brooder house, from which they had had free access to good pasture throughout the summer, to the laying pens which we had enlarged to house them properly, scouring and cleaning every crack and cranny as thoroughly as one would in one's own house. The birds were heavy. Alfred would take eight, I'd start out with six and end up carrying four. This, our first year with a larger flock, we had to learn so many things the hard way. With the chickens crowded in corners like frightened people, a number would die from suffocation. The second night we were on hand at dusk to put the birds on roosts. That was an endless chore. I'm sure we put each bird on the roost at least ten times before it stayed there. It was a perfect slimming exercise.

The poultry business, as we were learning it, was fraught with difficulties that made its economic value uncertain, and it took up a lot of time. As the chickens grew, carrying water from the barn to the garage demanded more energy than I cared to give. That chore was drudgery to both of us, yet we never failed to have fresh water always available for them. But the chore was not as heavy when the water had only to be carried into the laying pens, and we soon forgot the summer's toil, particularly when at the end of the year, in spite of the high mortality rate, the books showed a profit, and we still had the flock laying well, and could sell them when they stopped producing.

Now we wanted to get our next baby chicks earlier to catch the high prices for eggs in August. Our farm programme didn't allow for any more equipment, and we would be unable to let the chicks out until they were quite big, so we figured 250 was all the brooder house could hold. Buying 250 chicks in February and 300 more in April ought to work out quite well, so that's what we planned for. With chicken wire I built little secluded areas in the brooder house where I placed doubtful looking chicks. We had read of the use of the sulpha drugs in combating coccidiosis. I found out the dosage and ordered a supply. At the first sign of droopiness, the whole flock was treated according to directions, and the mortality rate dropped to nil. I have since read of and practiced the building of immunity by allowing the chicks to be exposed to the coccidiosis germs. This is done by not changing the paper the first two days in the brooder. They cannot be protected entirely from infection in any case, and sulpha drugs are expensive. Building immunity is not only cheaper, but produces a healthier layer.

The first lot of 250 chicks weren't so big when it came time to move them out, therefore it was easy to carry them from brooder house to chicken house. This was another new area we'd fixed for them, extending from the original chicken house through a straw shed, a driving shed and a new area built over our new pig pen. Here the old hens would not be disturbed as they gradually terminated their laying period. Here again we had scrubbed and scoured so that not a germ would live to harm our precious flock. The brooder house also had to be scoured and cleaned for the next lot of 300. It was a lot of work again, and not particularly attractive to either of us. We were not satisfied with the profits compared with the work involved or the thriftiness of the layers.

The following year we decided to buy chicks with the idea of selling hatching eggs. Having had my experience with roosters flying at me, I wasn't too happy about the prospect, but we wanted the extra money, and I was ready to take my chances.

Nothing seemed to go right. The pullets were not as uniform as we would have liked. The work with the eggs, having to weigh each one, increased our working hours, and this we didn't like at all. Our baby chicks bought in January had suffered some mishandling in the hatchery, and succumbed like flies under a spray till only a few unhealthy little birds remained, and these had to be destroyed in their first week of life. We stopped selling hatching eggs, sold the roosters and, dissatisfied with the production, sold the entire laying flock with the exception of twenty-odd for house use. This was bad. We had counted heavily on our poultry profits for farm improvement, and now we had to buy an entire new lot of started chicks to have layers in the summer when the prices would be high.

We made another mistake. We bought white birds, and too many for the space they would have to be confined in. The result was something we'd read about, but never seen before, and I hope will never see again. Cannibalism. The flock was brought down to size suitable to the quarters so rapidly by the chickens themselves that we despaired of having any left by the time they would start to lay.

We soon learned that once blood had been drawn, the chicken would be devoured so rapidly nothing could save it. So we visited the pen at frequent intervals and swooped down in close competition with the flock on every bird we spied a drop of blood on, knowing we might as well dress it and eat it, for it would in a few minutes be killed by its mates, and we weren't hungry enough to eat a bird we found dead. Chicken was our main meat course for a month, and we didn't use half of them. They carried their habit into the laying pens; but here we put in practice a method of combatting cannibalism we had learned from a farmer friend. A teaspoonful of salt per hundred birds in their drinking water once a week! It worked for us.

In April the early chicks that had been sacrificed to handling in the hatchery were replaced. We'd learned a lot about chickens the hard way again.

With the new lot we changed our feeding programme. It was more expensive, but the birds were healthier, and when they started to lay, production was improved.

I had a pet, a golden Hamp Rock who had flown up to my shoulder ever since it was tiny. Now, moved to the laying pens, she'd come to meet me, jump up on the pail, then on my head, and I'd feed her from my hand. This was Susy, whom I was very careful never to watch for too closely when culling time came. Alfred promised never to kill her for the house. I could never have eaten Susy.

Our feeding methods were pretty well in hand and, apart from the cost, quite satisfactory. Also, the brand of chickens we like best had been settled upon, and we had our enlarged chicken house. All this gave us a secure feeling about our poultry enterprise.

Alfred's winter reading kept us watchful. We spent long hours discussing ideas obtained. Keeping the poultry house dry and cleared out was a big job and crippling to Alfred, who had had his back injured during the war and found cleaning stables and shovelling manure one of the hardest chores he had to do. On several occasions he had been laid up for days after cleaning stables. It was one occupation that had to be changed. I longed to see him with a proper litter carrier system, but that was too expensive right now. The next best was hired help for short periods, and I finally persuaded him to agree to this.

There was a lot of literature on deep litter about this time which sounded practical. We decided to try it for the cattle as well as the chickens.

Getting the laying pens cleared out for the new flock had always been a lot of hard work, repulsive to both of us. Alfred had read about the merits of Vitamin B 12, how it was manufactured in the cow's stomach and transmitted through the manure; that chickens allowed the freedom of the barnyard were freer from disease than any confined. We had to keep our laying flock confined, but we could take the Vitamin B 12 to it. Further reading and our inability to be absolutely sure the laying pens were sterilized convinced us that all this disinfecting and scrubbing may kill all the harmful bacteria, but it also kills the benevolent bacteria which should be allowed to live. We decided to try an experiment with our new flock.

The laying pen was cleared out, but not disinfected. A thick bed of new, clean straw was put down, and in one corner a big shovel full of cow manure. Then we moved our pullets in. Instead of cleaning the chicken house frequently, the manure was kept dry by adding more straw, until doors we used to walk through standing upright we had to bend almost double to pass through. The chicken pen was cleared out once a year. The corner where the cow manure had been thrown was scratched to the bare boards innumerable times, and the birds were healthier and had the lowest mortality and highest egg production yet.

We were convinced the first winter we tried the easier method that it was right, and have not deviated from this procedure since. That was the winter of 1950-1951. We also changed our feeding methods. Perhaps the companies who mix feeds and mashes for poultry will not care for this little bit of information, but many of those who have tried it have come back specially to thank us for the tip.

The importance of protein in feeding caught Alfred's interest; also the fact that the requirements of any animal or human being for physical health vary with the individual. If the chickens were given free choice, each bird would eat what it required, one more, another less. Why feed mashes that contained only 18 per cent protein, when putting the concentrate which is 36 per cent protein in front of them they could balance their own ration? We tried it, and have continued this feeding method ever since. Again, the birds are healthier and lay bigger, better eggs for a longer period coming up in production more slowly but holding the peak for a longer period and declining slowly.

So, why pay $5.00 or more per cwt. for laying mash containing only 18 per cent protein and a lot of cheap fillers, when for about 25 per cent more cost you can obtain 100 per cent more protein?

Somewhere we read of one man's experience in finding, by feeding whole grain, the chickens weren't infested with worms; the coarse hulls keeping the intestinal track clear. Apart from deworming them before they are first put in the laying pens, we have had no other trouble with worms, and the chickens are fed whole grain, which also eliminates the cost of cracking and handling, giving yet another small per cent of net profit. They have free access to poultry concentrate, kept in front of them at all times; grit and oyster shell with plenty of fresh water. When we had mangels, I delighted in sticking some on nails conveniently placed if only to watch the chickens rush them. I gave them molasses too, one winter, which they loved.

Our best method of feeding, most economical and productive, was yet to come. Grass silage. When Alfred opened the silo, he tossed a fork of silage to the chickens out of curiosity. At first they shied away, gingerly pecking the strange looking stuff. It didn't take long, however, for them to be waiting expectant near the door for their morning ration. Alfred gave them all they could clear up by noon. We found this cut their concentrate requirements in half, thus lowering our feeding costs tremendously.

There are some who are sure the eggs must be green, because of our method of feeding. I assure you this is not so. The eggs are, if anything, higher in nutrition value; at least they are much more satisfying. The extra large percentage has increased, with very few eggs graded lower than A Large.

We now have accommodation for 1,400 layers, running water in all the pens, and are still doubtful about the value of artificial light during the shorter days. When we first started we had no electricity, and talked of how much better it would be for our layers when we could put lights in the chicken house.

Although the barn was wired for our pressure system and there are lights in the barn in case we need them—and in the pig pens, which are like a maternity ward—we still have not put lights in the laying pens. Our flock does not go into a moult during its laying peak. By not forcing them, we think we avoid a lot of trouble, and make a tidy profit as well on our enterprise. There is a limit to all things, and pushing too hard may not be as economical as it appears. You can't quite put a chicken on a production quota. She is liable to go on strike. So, after years of study, trial and error, we have streamlined our poultry industry along these lines.

We have bought chickens from the first of January every month through till May, and we have tried eight different breeds, settling at last on Hamp Rock pullets, bought the first week in May. Buying them at that time, they are $2.00 a hundred cheaper, and this more than pays for the fuel oil used in brooding them. The weather is warm and they are outside within three weeks, with the brooder stoves turned off.

For the next five months, till the middle of October, when they are 5 ½ months old, they are out on range—good pasture, changed every year—on a predominating grain ration with a limited quantity of growing ration, developing large strong bodies. Then they are moved to the laying pens, which have only been empty for six, weeks, and inside of a fortnight they are starting production. Not with predominating peewee eggs, which we had always had to contend with from early hatched chicks, but with less than one per cent peewees on the first two crates of eggs, and a very large percentage of medium and large. We get a rapid increase in production, and by the first of December our hens are up to 65 per cent.

Our flock maintains its 65 per cent, gradually rising to 70 per cent by the first of January, and as the days lengthen out production increases until by the first of April they have reached as high as 85 per cent one year and 90 per cent another, just when eggs are becoming expensive again. With a very slow tapering off of 95 per cent large and extra large eggs during the high prices of the summer months, when we really make money out of our chickens, by the first of August they are down to 50 per cent production, and by very close culling that is maintained until the early part of September.

The whole flock is moved out just before going into a moult, after ten months laying of never below 50 per cent production and as high as 90 per cent.

Our feeding method with this laying flock has been to feed western oats with 10 per cent wheat and barley and which the flock will clean up in two hours after feeding. 36 per cent concentrate is kept in hoppers before them, and this feeding programme takes over as soon as the pullets go in the laying pens. When the trench silo is opened for the cattle, the chicken ration is supplemented with grass silage, and this cuts consumption of concentrate in half, without affecting the egg production.

Consider the costs of production in a three-month period, December, January and February, during which we produced eggs for 16 cents a dozen; a worthwhile result from hours of study and observation. The deep litter that has accumulated for the past ten months is cleaned out and spread on the fields before it has time to heat. There is but one cleaning a year, and no disinfecting. The walls are whitewashed occasionally to keep the pens bright.

CHAPTER 13

The centre stabling had been torn down the previous winter and the deep litter system used to great advantage in that it kept the smaller number of cattle warmer, and the manure taken direct from barn to field had proved its worth in the mangle crop and new seed that year. It was hard to clean out by hand, even with hired help for this chore. It took me a year to persuade Alfred to have a litter-carrier put in. With a winter's accumulation of manure to look at each time he was in the barn, it wasn't too hard to persuade him. Pigs had paid well; we had a little money. So, a happy contented wife prepared meals for the two men who installed the equipment that would save Alfred's back considerably. A fitting beginning to a wonderful year for us, putting in labour-saving devices. We could look back over the years when we struggled, blindly following the accustomed methods that promised only hardship and probably failure. For this soil of ours, so depleted, had to be given drastic rejuvenating treatment, or be included in the ever - increasing acreage known as marginal, run-out, worthless. Our soil had been exploited to the limit of its endurance; the buildings would soon have given the passer-by more visible evidence of its poverty. Like the hero in a fairy tale, Alfred came along just in time, equipped with the intelligence to see the need, seek the remedy, and with the moral stamina to apply it.

It is understandable, as the result of giving to the soil and seeing its bounteous return, that we should feel a deep peace and awareness of God in everything round about us.

Jim asks, "Mother, where is God?"

With a full heart, I reply, "He is everywhere, dear. In you and me, the soil, the birds and trees. We only have to let Him out. Watch what your Daddy is doing, giving food to the soil, and see what is given in return. We must do that in everything, let God out by doing the right and kind thing to people, animals, the trees, and the soil. In return, you will get abundant life."

One fine spring morning Alfred went out to the front field with his one-way disc to prepare a field on which he had sown sweet clover as a cover crop. He was preparing it for spring seeding to grain as a nurse crop, and a carefully planned grass and legume mixture of brome alfalfa and Ladino clover. A five-acre plot at the front was to be seeded down to a mixture of brome and alfalfa, a test plot for the Wellington County Soil and Crop Improvement Association.

Mr. Don Black, our Agricultural Representative for the County, came in with the seed mixture, when Alfred was about half finished one-way discing the field.

"What are you doing there?"

"Discing in sweet clover. This is the field for the test plot."

"What are you sowing the rest of it to?"

"Brome alfalfa and Ladino."

Mr. Black had come with fifteen minutes to spare from his busy day. He stayed for a couple of hours to watch what Alfred was doing. This brought to our minds the memory of Alfred's two visits to the Agricultural Representative's office, asking to have someone come over to look at our land and advise us. They were busy and understaffed, no doubt, but they never did get around to it. Finally, knowing that we were definitely on our own, Alfred said:

"They will come to me one day, but I'll never go back again and ask them to come."

Mr. Black was interested, and our evening was enthusiastically spent discussing the conversations of the afternoon. Alfred has always shared these with me, patiently recounting all that was said, so I am kept in constant touch with the practice of agriculture on the farm, and its results. This helps tremendously in seeing what is most important and being able, without fuss, argument, or misunderstanding, to go about doing first things first, spending our "Doings" on the most important things, knowing the frills and luxuries we dream of are sure to come in their own good time.

The following day at noon, after we had finished dinner, when Alfred was greasing up the tractor, a young man appeared.

"Are you Mr. Leatherbarrow?"

"Yes."

"I'm Frank Fischer of the Veterans' Land Act."

"What do you beggars want?" was the blunt reply.

Nonplussed, Frank said,: "I met Don Black in Guelph last night and he told me you were doing some very interesting work here and if I wanted to see it, to come up right away."

Alfred smiled; then he explained his blunt reception and the two men set out to look at and discuss all the methods of cultivation on the farm, returning to the house late in the afternoon for tea and further discussion.

Frank had not known of our being turned down as a poor risk by the V.L.A. Although Alfred assured him they were quite right in turning us down, we did need the assistance badly at the beginning, and it was still a slightly sore point with us, having been hampered so by lack of capital.

"Would you take it now, if you could get it?"

"Certainly. I'd be a fool not to accept more capital which I can use to advantage. We are over the hump now, but I won't cut off my nose to spite my face."

"Well, if I've anything to do with it, you'll get it. We need you now."

Frank left as dusk was falling, leaving us with our minds full of figuring as to what we'd do with the extra capital—capital that we'd never dreamed of having.

The old Buick with radiator trouble that nobody could cure would need a new set of tires, if we were to use it much longer. It had passed its usefulness, having fulfilled a long period of constant use as a school bus before we bought it. The previous summer, when we went to Fenelon Falls for a long week-end over Civic Holiday, our first away from the farm for a long period, the car had limped from gas station to gas station, from country pump to country pump, always having to have its radiator filled with water in spite of the pills it had been given to clear its pipes. It was like a Stanley Steamer; at least that is what we called it when a cloud of steam would blur our vision and we would have to stop till it cooled down. That was a long trip. The Buick should be replaced.

The front field was rapidly fitted and seeded by one-way discing, once cultivating, and seeding with the recommended fertilizer. The front five acres were seeded to the Soil and Crop Improvement mixture, and the balance to Alfred's chosen mixture, having one strip unfertilized to get a proper picture of the value of fertilizer. Now, Alfred was working in the back field where we had had such a bumper crop of grain; one-way discing preparatory to seeding. He had gone back directly after dinner. We had been held up by a visit to the V.L.A. office in Guelph for our formal interview regarding our renewed application for V.L.A. aid, and Alfred didn't want to be any later getting his crop planted.

I was in the kitchen washing dishes at a table beside the window. I liked to look out at the flower-bed Alfred had made for me one day while I was away, as a surprise. All the world was rosy. We'd taken the iron monster down in the living-room. Now it didn't have to be kept lit all the time for warmth, when the fire place would give us all we needed and look much more attractive. I'd be outside most of the time from now till fall and loved the thought.

A glitter of chrome suddenly nosed its way into my vision and I wondered: "Who's the big shot visiting us now?"

I dried my hands. Anything could happen. I felt like Cinderella. At any rate, the man was accustomed to the practice of farmers. He came to the back door. A smiling jovial friendly man.

"Mrs. Leatherbarrow?"

"Yes."

"I'm Mr. McKinnon from Hoskings Motors. I have a Buick here I'd like to sell your husband. We'd like to see all the farmers in Wellington County driving Buicks."

"We drive a Buick."

He laughed.

"So I see."

He'd seen our Buick standing tired-looking under the crab-apple tree. I grinned.

"I don't think Alfred will be interested. We planned on buying a car in the fall, but not now."

I hesitated. This was mean, to dangle a lovely looking car under Alfred's nose who longed to drive a nice one. Still, he should have the doubtful pleasure of turning down the offer.

"I'll make him an offer he can't resist," said Mr. McKinnon.

I grinned again and thought, "Brother, you don't know my Alfred. He can resist anything he decides to."

"He's working in the back field," I said. "You can drive down the lane, turn left over the hill at the end of the lane, follow the path through the grass and you will see him."

I went back to the dishes, my thoughts mingled with pity and delight. I didn't like dangling anything attractive just out of Alfred's reach, yet he was the only one to judge whether we could or could not manage a new car.

In his discussions with Frank Fischer about the amount of money he'd receive when our application went through, as we were assured it definitely would this time, the two men had differed, Alfred certain we would get $480 less than Frank assured us we would get, but it was pleasant to count, not too seriously, on the extra.

I finished up the dishes just as the grey and chrome car drew up beside the house and Alfred, beaming, stepped out from behind the wheel. My heart disappeared somewhere inside my body and on watery legs I met him at the door.

"It's a beauty; less than we planned we could spend in the fall. Will I take it?"

"If you think we can manage it, yes."

He went out to dicker; a pastime he never tired of and did very well at, much to my satisfaction because I'm the opposite. The telephone rang.

"Guelph calling, Alfred." I ran out, excited. "It's Frank Fischer, Alfred." And I stood watching Alfred's face as he talked, reading in it what I longed to hear.

"The application has been O.K.'d, and what's more, Frank was right. I get the extra $480."

With this assurance and extra capital we had not expected, Alfred completed his bargain.

"I'll drive the old Buick back to Guelph; you drive the new one around over the week-end and if you don't want it, bring it in Monday and drive your old one home," said Mr. McKinnon.

"Fair enough."

Mr. McKinnon and his companion drove off in the old Buick with a dignity befitting her exit from our life, each smoking big cigars. They were hardly out of sight when Alfred, Jim and I slipped into the newer, luxurious, deluxe model and drove up to our friend Earl Maben's garage for a complete check-up. I regaled Olive, his wife, with our good fortune while the two men put the car through its paces, finding nothing wrong.

The following morning we drove in unthought-of luxury to Guelph to complete the sale and hear our friendly agent recount his journey of terror driving the old Buick to its final resting place. Alfred got another $50 knocked off the price when the deal was completed. It was Saturday, and in the evening we would go to Fergus to play bridge with Mother and Dad.

No queen felt more regal than I, sitting beside my king, with our little prince beaming in the back. As we nosed over the hill down the main street of my home town, I told Alfred of how as a young girl I had always dreamed of coming home with my Prince Charming in a beautiful car, and now that dream had come true, for I could not have felt more like that young romantic girl than I did now, clasping my husband's hand, tingling with delight on the seat beside me.

The Pipe Band was assembling for its weekly parade up and down the main street. A drummer waved us on as we stopped behind them.

"Let's wait and follow them," I whispered.

I love the bagpipes and hate to miss hearing them whenever I can. We waited, and so were led in our new car down the main street of Fergus by my favourite pipe band. The only flaw, I didn't see a soul I knew to wave to as we passed slowly down the street.

There wasn't much bridge played that night as we regaled Dad and Mother with our enthusiastic tales of the events of the past week, the first of many exciting developments to come.

The garage would have to give up its poultry occupants to house this lovely car, but that was going to work out all right too, for we had already decided May chicks were our best buy and the car could then stay outside for the summer. Everything was wonderful. We were on top of the world.

CHAPTER 14

On May 23rd another visitor drove in from the Ontario Crops, Weeds and Seeds Branch of the Department of Agriculture, a very friendly chap whom we got to know and like in no time at all. He arrived shortly after dinner and ran for his car at six o'clock, having walked the farm with Alfred, losing all sense of time in their interesting discussion of crops and farming.

He not only admired the wonderful catch of new seeds evident, but remarked while standing in the top field of orchard grass and alfalfa, "I haven't seen anything as good yet, this year. If I hadn't seen it, I wouldn't have believed it. Why, this is only the 23rd of May, not the 23rd of June."

The rich grass of the front field was seeded the same year. Every other farmer in the district had plowed under his same seeding, because of a poor catch. This caught our visitor's interest, as Alfred told the story.

"I listened to Dr. Weir of O.A.C., at one of our Crop Improvement meetings, tell of the experiments made with manure in Europe the year I was going to seed this field down. I had used the centre stable as a loafing barn for young cattle and it was full of just the right un-leached material to try the experiment for myself. I'd also read some of Edward Faulkner's theory on trash farming, and knew I had to do something different on this land if I counted to stay on it. I hauled the manure direct from the stable to the field in the spring just before seeding time and cultivated it in, seeding immediately after. I was told by various neighbours I was crazy, that it was the wrong way. I could see they hadn't had any remarkable results from their methods of farming, while I was willing to try something new, particularly when it sounded so reasonable. The result was, I was the only farmer in the district with a good catch that year."

Alfred came in that night, eyes shining. He'd had a wonderful afternoon asking and answering questions, giving a little information and getting a lot in return. At last we had something to give.

It was a warm evening. As we sat in the living-room and talked about the new developments and the interest shown by people who know farming, our hearts sang. But we decided that we would not be able to indulge in the luxury of our shower baths that summer. There was too much risk of someone surprising us. We laughed. It had taken us five years to discover the full use of a watering can. As the dream bathroom looked closer to our reach, we could waive that pleasure for this year.

But one hot day after giving Jim his shower and seeing the little body glisten as the stream of water held high above his head carried the mucky suds so full of good earth off his cool, clean skin, we, sticky also, succumbed once more to our old luxury.

Alfred held the watering can for me and I for him.

We had just finished when a sound sent us scrambling for towels and the house. It was nothing, but we knew we'd never chance it again. Our seclusion and anonymity were gone, replaced by new interests to which we must adjust ourselves and our living; ever careful to keep guarded the sanctity of home and our life together.

The location of the pit silo was decided upon for several reasons, the chief one to eliminate work. Alfred didn't want to have to haul silage to the cattle. The only pit silos he had seen had this disadvantage. Good drainage was also important. The harvester he had bought from the McKee Brothers unloaded as well as loaded, so no further expense was necessary other than fitting a wagon with high sides and back. It could be the one-man operation we sought.

Mack Neilson came out and dug the silo. A pit was dug flush with the stone foundation of the barn, where it would open into the root cellar, running straight out through the old vegetable garden sixty-five feet, with sloping sides from a fourteen foot width at the top tapering to ten feet at the bottom. It was cut through sand, the sides of which Alfred sliced smooth, thus allowing good drainage and packing too, on open bottom that supplied the natural drainage so necessary in a good pit silo.

We were ready to begin. Excited, not a little; apprehensive, yes! Alfred arranged with a neighbouring lad to work for us that summer, so that in our first year with the new equipment and method he would have ready help if needed. As our silage programme was started long before haying, the boy had free time for this period when his father didn't need him.

Gerald and Russell McKee delivered the harvester in person and stayed to put it into operation, the first of its kind used for this purpose. Everyone was interested, including the V.L.A. Six field supervisors came in during the day to watch operations and, unable to contain myself at the house, I followed the men up over the hill. We passed the waving wheat field that gratified us in its abundance, sure proof that the procedure of returning a green crop to the soil had been right.

The previous Sunday, on our weekly walk round the farm, Alfred and I had gone through the wheat field to see the state of the soil where different methods and seeds had been used. Where the open summer fallow had been the soil was dry and hard and had wide cracks half an inch or more in width. Where the oats had been, the soil showed signs of moisture coming to the surface. The cracks were fewer and not more than a quarter of an inch in width. Where the buckwheat had been, there were no cracks. Here moisture was evident. The soil was crumbly, full of organic matter and the grain thick and strong stemmed, ample repayment for the previous year's crop sacrifice. All this, the V.L.A. men noted as they passed. The crop showed no evidence of a run-out farm now, and when they saw the new seed thick with red clover, one remarked, "You couldn't chase a rabbit through." They now knew that Alfred's methods were good.

The machine was starting on the orchard grass and alfalfa, a good thick crop, still improving, having been seeded in 1947 as a short term mixture. The winter of 1950-1951, Alfred had manured most of it. So, all was in readiness to start on the "top of the world" field where all could see and hear for vast distances around. The V.L.A. men, interested, critical, sat in a row close by.

The McKees and Alfred, confident yet apprehensive, would have preferred to be alone to watch it start. They went right ahead, setting everything in motion. The old 10-20 tractor, with its new dignity, a power take-off, started. The machine set in motion, its fans caused a roaring sound we were unaccustomed to, loud in our ears. Everyone watched and listened, tense and anxious. Into this operation we had put our all, money, planned programme, the future of the farm.

It went ten feet and clogged up. Russ and Gerald worked rapidly and critically to clear it, ten feet more and again it stopped. This went on till one by one the V.L.A. men left, and sensing the dejection of Alfred and the McKees, I left them also alone with their brain child, their pet, their problem.

Back to the house with a proud glance over the golden wheat.

"Alfred is never wrong," I thought. "The machine will work. I am glad they are alone to figure it out."

So the boys loaded the harvester on the truck and took it back to Elmira where they installed a jeep engine to augment the power of our old 10-20, and brought it back two days later. That was what it needed—more power to keep the pick-up clear. But that did not end all the troubles. The radiator clogged with chaff, causing it to boil and be a constant working hazard to the men, too often too close for safety, in danger of being burned by steam. Every trip the radiator had to be filled with water. It wasted time. In fact, just about everything that could happen to delay the filling of the silo did happen. Alfred was sure a lot of it would be spoiled this our first year. Perseverance kept them going, and soon it would be filled with a good forty per cent grass and sixty per cent legume mixture.

It took me all day to do my few chores, watching the silo filling and our new machine at work. Like a small child, I lost all sense of time and watched, fascinated and delighted to see Alfred accomplishing what he had planned to do, in spite of the troubles he had to overcome to do it.

Talking with a Cockshutt dealer, the McKees told of the power difficulties Alfred had with his old 10-20 and the new harvester, and that he would probably be in the market for a new tractor. The dealer asked to demonstrate.

"Sure, but I'm not buying a tractor this year," Alfred said.

"That's all right."

So a nice new Cockshutt 40 came on our farm, to draw the harvester and wagon with ease over the slopes that had taken all the 10-20 had to offer with the jeep assistance. It was like the contrast between the two Buicks.

"Keep it over the week-end," said the dealer.

We did and Alfred tried it out with the one-way disc, where he was cutting in a sweet clover crop that had grown higher than the tractor stood, averaging five feet in height over all the field. He finished the field, drove the tractor back to the side of the house, reluctant to get off, lest the next time it started it would be to go back to Elmira where it belonged. Sunday, we looked admiringly at it and noted all the good features our own old model lacked. Jim, like a little button, sat proudly on the seat pretending to drive, and Alfred hitched the harvester and wagon on behind for me to take a picture of Jim "playing at work."

"I hate to see it go off the place."

"Then don't let it go," I said.

"Oh, I can't buy that now."

"Just sit down and figure it out. You'll be able to."

Alfred figured. This would have to be a deal involving some tall dickering. When the agent returned, Alfred made him a proposition, and the contest was on.

The old tractor, ten young cattle and a small note, plus a dozen eggs, left the tractor on the place. Alfred's dickering ability at its best! We were mechanized efficiently and well, long before we had ever dreamed it possible. Off balance, yes, but with greatly improved production per acre. The ability to feed more cattle assured our economic position. It was so vastly improved that the risk in mechanizing was eliminated by the possibilities of future increased production and lowered costs.

Mack Neilson was back again to combine the wheat. Alfred had him cut it high, and the following day Alfred one-way disced the wheat straw into the field, the next day sowing oats on the trashy crumbly soil. Three weeks later our thirty-two cattle were turned into pasture. They had free access to good alfalfa and orchard grass, but showed a very definite preference for the young oats, returning to them and remaining there for longer periods than they spent anywhere else on the farm.

Young oats, Alfred had read, were twenty-six per cent protein, higher than any other pasture forage, and our young cattle
thrived well on it. So this year we were harvesting two crops,
making up for the previous year when there was no crop taken
off the field; wheat that ran fifty bushels to the acre, and two
and a half months pasture on a high protein feed, as well as
leaving a cover crop to stop erosion, and top soil run-off with
the following spring rain.

All the grain which had been grown this year as a nurse
crop for new seed was combined and with our new harvester
Alfred picked up the straw and blew it with ease into the mows.
The dry hay had also been handled this way. My days of hay
making were over. Thinking back at how well we managed, I
feel proud to have been a link in the successful operations on
our farm, glad to have been actively involved in every operation
that now, I knew, I would never be able to do again.

This gave us more time and freedom to enjoy the pleasures
we liked. Farming was beginning to be what we had always
striven to make it, a wonderful way of life, free from hours of
heartbreaking work and drudgery. The power company people
notified us to get the farm wired. This we did. It was in August,
and the "Doings" had been stretched to take in the tractor and
car before we had planned for either, but everything was working out well and we were filled with optimism for a glowing
future.

It was Saturday night again. I had pre-emptied the wallet
of all but two dollars. Tomorrow was my birthday and Alfred
and Jim would be getting extravagant ideas in the shops that
night. On the main corner, as we prepared to separate and do
our shopping in order to save time in getting over to Fergus for
a game, Alfred asked for the wallet, which I had in my purse.
Perhaps I gave it to him too willingly, for suspicion filled his
eyes.

"How much money is there in it?"

"Plenty."

"Let me see. Two dollars!" and, with a mock severity that
would have made any passerby pity me had they heard,

"Give me that money."

I was beaten, and handed over my loot. The two conspirators were off and I was left wondering what desire I could pos-

sibly have allowed myself to mention in the past that would lead Alfred to spend all our money recklessly tonight. I learned later that he had gone into Lloyd's hardware store and been shown a refrigerator which he had not gone in with the intention of buying.

"I'll buy it on one condition," he said, "It must be delivered immediately."

"You mean Monday morning, of course."

"I mean within the next hour. Tomorrow is Margaret's birthday."

Directions were given and followed to the letter. It was put in the living room and the kitchen door closed, while we were in Fergus. We returned home earlier than usual; my men were just like children expecting Santa Claus.

As was our custom, and it's a horrible one, we entered the house via the kitchen.

"Don't go in the living room," I was admonished.

So I didn't. But they couldn't wait till morning. Finally we all went in, and there, in the middle of the living room floor stood a beautiful refrigerator. I was stunned.

"Open it up. Look inside."

Here I found an outfit for decorating cakes, a hobby of mine that I'd followed the hard way with wax paper funnels, for birthdays; and a cake mix. Jim, our small son, had promised me that.

"Daddy and I will make your birthday cake tomorrow, mother."

"My darling!" I was speechless.

"You have helped me, and now that I have all this good equipment," said Alfred, "there should be something that will be nice for you in the house."

Civic Holiday! In our nice new Buick, we followed Mack Neilson with his combine down the lane. We we're off for a gala summer week-end at our honeymoon cottage. This time there would be plenty of companionship there, at the main cottage. Our hired man would take care of the few chores. Our pig pens were empty, in carrying out Alfred's plan to eliminate all chance of rhinitis existing there. He hoped one day to keep brood sows.

Alfred was smoking a big cigar, and we turned to beam at
Mack as we slowed down on the brow of the hill to wave and
call, "Goodbye Friendship. We will be back."

It was a plutocrat's week-end, like the honeymoon of two-
and-a-half months we had enjoyed there. We had no worries
then, but we were like a rudderless ship. Now, with direction
fixed and proven methods, our worries would be mild, short-
lived and remediable.

We were equally glad to be home again; busy with our
enterprise. Home, that magic place where we are fortunate
enough to be able to eat, sleep and work our whole life through.
The electricians came in and told us to get wired. The power
would be brought in soon after, and then my new refrigerator
could be put to use.

In the kitchen, under the old lamp shelf now stood a four-
burner electric stove. Alfred was overwhelming me with gifts
and consideration; saying thanks the best way he could for all
the years during which we had gone without the simple conveniences taken for granted in the city. This was wonderful, so
much so I wondered if I was really awake, not dreaming it all.
But no, it hurt when I pinched myself. God's in His Heaven.
All's right with the world.

Daisy and Tommy were coming up for a week-end. After
that we would settle down to a pleasant winter of planning for
the following year. The V.L.A. were truly interested in all Alfred
was doing. Someone was constantly coming in to talk. Early in
January they were having a convention in Guelph and would
like to bring the Director for Canada to visit us.

"Sure. That will be fine. Bring him along."

It was forgotten temporarily in the business of each day.
We had men from the office in London on various occasions,
and were getting to know and like them and have interesting
conversations with them all. Alfred did not feel so alone in what
he was doing, for now there were people intelligently interested
and giving him encouragement.

Daisy brought her movie camera again and we took pictures all over the farm—the cattle, a number of little whitefaced
Herefords Alfred had bought early in the summer to replace
those traded on the tractor and to utilize the good pasture we
now had in abundance; the cats, all twelve of them, with Ace

jealous each time I picked one up—I, who used to dislike cats and dogs so much; feeding the chickens. That was when a suspicion I had not wanted to harbour became a certainty.

"Alfred, I'm sure something has happened. There are not nearly as many chickens as there should be."

He looked them over carefully. "No, you are right."

Then we moved them and counted them, surmising that during our holiday week-end at least one hundred and fifty had been stolen. It had been a happy but expensive holiday. This year, when we had counted so on every source of income that we had, any loss was great.

Earlier in the spring before the new Buick replaced the old, Alfred and I had gone several times to Flora-dale to find a man who did bulldozing. The old permanent pasture so barren and, apart from the running water all summer long, useless, was to be smoothed off and worked; brought at last under cultivation. Finally, a contractor for a large firm was contacted and he sent in two bulldozers who did the work in thirty hours. Three hundred dollars!

Alfred and the man hired to help him cleared stone off the cleaner section and disced it many times to level it, cultivating and harrowing till smooth. Eight of the sixteen acres were sown to wheat without fertilizer. Alfred was curious to learn what the fertility was like on this virgin soil.

It was to be a winter of careful management of our resources. We were rich in equipment and conveniences and increased production of our soil, but temporarily low in financial returns.

It was to be our first Christmas with lights for our tree. These I had carefully stored away from my years of light housekeeping while working in Toronto, or we would not have had them.

Jim's Christmas we took care of. Our own we agreed to forget, remembering all the good things we had received throughout the year. But it was no good. We loved giving each other gifts. The family were not coming out to dinner. We would be alone. Alfred put little slips of paper on the tree with promises written on them. I had a handknit pair of socks I'd worked on in the early morning hours while he still slept. Oblivious, I hope, of our despondency, Jim enjoyed his gifts, grateful as the dear, wee lad has always been for anything given him. The crowning mishap of the day was to have the Christmas tree lights go out. We had counted on them for cheerfulness, and we had no spare bulbs. It was our low ebb, yet we knew in our hearts there was nothing to feel low about. Rather the contrary. A rosy, interesting future, brighter even than either of us dreamed possible at the time, lay ahead. The little gift slips consisted of promises for "a dishwashing," a "breakfast in bed," an "egg cleaning," etc., and Alfred fulfilled them all.

Later in the winter, while Alfred was doing some expert carpentry work in the house, I went to the barn alone to feed the chickens and gather the eggs as was my wont. I had brought my pails of grain, which I scattered on the deep litter, and had brought a pail of concentrate to fill up the hoppers, that the chickens might never be without. Just as I tipped the pail, bending forward slightly to do so, I was paralyzed by a crippling pain in my back. I couldn't straighten up. There was nothing to hold on to. The pail dropped. Carefully and slowly I surveyed my position. The walls were all too far away to reach with an outstretched arm, and in my position I couldn't keep my balance without support. To fall in the chicken house and not be able to get up terrified me. The chickens might pick me to pieces. I could visualize that never-forgotten bloody orgy of cannibalism, and gave these harmless looking birds my fearful respect.

"Alfred! Alfred!" I called, knowing of course, he could not hear.

Panic seized me for a moment. Then common sense took over and, slowly and carefully, I stepped gingerly along the hopper to the end closest to a wall. Here, by sheer will power I forced my steps to reach the wall and, with it to support, found my way out of the inner room, back and around the first room to the door and out. A short rest and, with great relief to be away from the livestock, I felt my way out of the run-in shed and through the pumphouse, and literally crawled to the house.

For three days I remained a cripple, victim of my first, and I hope, last bout with lumbago. Carried to bed, I remained there a couple of days and spent my convalescence on the chesterfield in the living-room, disgusted with my state and anxious to be up and about again.

After that, Alfred never let me go to the barn alone, but planned always to be near at hand in case there was a recurrence.

With all the signs of an early winter showing on October 15th, Alfred, as curious as a child with his Christmas stocking, opened the silo. He found to his relief and amazement that there was very little spoilage. There was some close to the wall, where he broke through from the root cellar, and on top; but Alfred knew he could eliminate that the following year. So, in spite of all the delays and difficulties encountered during the silo filling, we had good ensilage to feed our stock. This Alfred commenced to do at once. The chickens got as much as they could handle in the forenoon. The cattle cleaned up every morsel of their portion, fed in the morning, with relish it was a pleasure to watch. I liked the pungent smell of the silage.

We talked with my brother-in-law, Dr. Ewing, of Grosse Pointe, Michigan, about the advantages of feeding silage. We knew alfalfa was high in protein, and how much better our poultry did on a free choice of concentrates than on commercial mashes lower in protein. Knowing, also, that the ensiling process started a chemical reaction and not knowing exactly what that was, and also that the silage contained a high protein feed in alfalfa, Alfred asked,

"What is the breakdown of protein and carbohydrate in silage?"

"Glucose."

This rang the bell. He remembered his days as a hospital patient, when so many patients, suffering from loss of blood and at low ebb following operations, were given glucose intravenously. This was rapidly assimilated into the bloodstream, and the patient responded favourably and well. Alfred thought of the nine feeder pigs he had housed in the horse stable to keep the pig pens empty for their rebuilding the following summer. Later, consulting with nutrition experts, he also learned that the ensiling process broke down the protein in grass silage into amino acids and these became protein again in the form of meat.

With this information in mind, Alfred was off on a new line of thinking, developing a theory since proven correct, that a pig can only assimilate sixty per cent of its food, the balance passing through in its manure, which means a definite loss to the farmer. If the protein and carbohydrate is already broken down into glucose and amino acids, in other words predigested, the pig can then assimilate 100 per cent of its feed. Therefore, their requirements are fulfilled with the amount of forage they can eat. Alfred also knew carbohydrate produced fat, protein meat, and meat is what Mrs. Consumer wants when she buys pork at the butcher shop.

By this time, one of the pigs, that up to now were not nearly as thrifty as we would like them to be, had gone off its hind quarters, which seemed to be paralyzed. The veterinary, out to cut some young steers, said there was no use doing anything for it. It would likely die; it was suffering from a mineral deficiency, and it would cost more to save it than it would be worth. Alfred had isolated the poor thing, because the other pigs were jumping on it and it lost miserably in the gluttonous race for the trough at eating time.

Remembering the discussion with Herb about the breakdown of nutrients in silage, and knowing that, while a pig could only assimilate sixty per cent of green pasture it could utilize more silage because of the breakdown already started, one morning Alfred threw some silage to the pigs, and they gobbled it up.

"That's interesting," he said. He continued the practice each day, eliminating the grain ration in the morning entirely, feeding only silage. This he also did for the isolated cripple, who startled us by regaining its faculties and soon returning to the pen in the old horse stable rigged up for this lot of pigs. They were a healthy lot. A shine came to their coats. The hair no longer stood up dry and dull. Abounding health was most noticeable.

The thriftiness we desired was there. Now Alfred was sure. The tentative marketing date he had written down beside the purchase price, and that we had previously despaired reaching, would be met. We bought the pigs September 20, shipped them January 14. They had been fed the usual pig ration of chop mixed with the correct amount of hog grower for their age and weight, dry feeding for a month until the silo was opened. Then silage became their morning ration entirely, with the same amount of chop at night as had been their previous ration at that hour. That is, it was not increased, because they were getting it just once a day, thus cutting the feeding costs in half.

Alfred had his trip to London between Christmas and New Year's for his routine medical. The day of the appointment we had the worst storm of the winter. We were up at five a.m., Alfred to do the chores, throw down to the barn floor enough hay for the cattle's evening meal in case he didn't get back in time, and give the pigs (that were getting too big for me to battle, walking amongst them with a pail of chop) both their silage and chop. They were cared for for the day except for water, which I could give them from the vantage point of the feed alley. All I would have to do was look after the chickens, throw down the hay and put it in the mangers. We would get along without asking someone to come in.

I wrapped a few cookies, which I placed in Alfred's coat pocket, he protesting and feeling lonely before he'd even left the house, a little worried about going such a distance with the idea of returning the same day when the weather was so unsettled.

I stood at the living-room window and watched the car headlights shine on the glistening snow sparkling like diamonds, a pure smooth sheet of iridescent white, until the grey shadow of the car passed the window. Alfred was waving and smiling toward me, and then he was gone, leaving two dark pencil strips on the virgin snow which I contemplated, feeling the loneliness and the emptiness of the house engulfing me. I watched through the grey morning light the golden ribbon with its deeper grey shadow following, as the car slid up over the hill and out of sight.

"Safe return, dear God. Bring him home safe."

Pushing the coffee pot forward, looking over the debris of breakfast dishes, picking up the wire toaster Alfred had made me for use in the coal fire, to hang it on its hook behind the stove, I hear Jim stirring upstairs. It is snowing harder. I go back to the living-room window and see the tracks that Alfred made are all closed in. We are alone. A little island of warmth in a sea of snow, white, cold, oppressive.

Jim went with me to feed the chickens and gather eggs. Alfred had carried up plenty of water for the house. I wouldn't have to do that. By noon, I didn't dare look out at the weather.

The wind blew. Often the barn was obliterated from view by the blizzard. The mailman did get through, however, and barring a hard tumble on a patch of snow-covered ice that left me nursing a painful thigh for a moment before rising, I got the mail and spread the reading of the paper over as much time as I possibly could.

At four, the deadline for feeding, there was nothing for it but to bundle Jim and myself up and, armed with baskets for eggs, head for the barn in that blizzard. It looked ten miles away.

"Where is Alfred?" my heart cried.

Only the need to hide my fears from Jim and go about our daily tasks in a normal way kept me from throwing myself on our bed and giving myself up to the doubtful luxury of despair and tears.

The chickens were fed, watered and the eggs gathered. I had, with cheerful little Jim's valuable assistance, pushed all the hay on the barn floor through the feed doors, and now I was just finished, standing in the far alley after throwing a fork of dry hay to the uncomplaining pigs, who were not going to get any feeding tonight. The cattle were munching contentedly. A warm sense of kinship with nature, soothing and gentle, that always came over me here gave me a security I had not felt in the house with Alfred not there and the howling wind making a din in my listening ears. Here I couldn't hear the wind or feel the cold. The stable was warm, the stock clean, well-bedded and fed, exuding a well-being that included Jim and me.

I was looking at the pigs and thinking, "They are different."

When I used to come down with Alfred to carry the lantern or just walk round with him and talk as he did the chores, the first moment we stepped into the stable at feeding time, a chorus, loud and insistent from the hungry pigs, always filled the air. Not even the gentle increase of sound from the placid cattle, as they stirred and moved about expectantly from manger to manger, finding their favoured spot to await the hay—succulent, well saved, green and sweet—they knew was coming soon, could be heard above the pigs' squealing.

But these pigs were not squealing. They were not sleeping either, but looked completely content, nosing curiously   the unaccustomed hay portion I'd soft-heartedly thrown in for them to chew on if they wished.

What makes one feel one is being watched by human eyes? A stillness, a suspended motion ran through the stable like an electric spark. I turned quickly, almost in fear, and there standing quietly, motionless, just inside the door of the first feed alley was my husband.

"Alfred, Alfred, you are home safe!"

I ran to his waiting arms. All the weight of worry, fear and apprehension born of the storm raging outside rolled away. My feet were like wings. I floated on joy.

"My, it's nice watching you taking such good care of the stock. I could stand there all day and watch you."

"Did you see me give the pigs some hay?"

"Yes."

"I felt sorry for them. But, do you know, they aren't squealing. They aren't hungry."

We both listened. Alfred helped finish feeding the hay and the pigs called for nothing. They were content to wait till morning.

"That silage must be wonderful stuff."

"Do you notice they aren't fat. They are growing well, but not fat."

"And the one that was paralyzed. I can't tell which one it is now."

"It's all better. All it lacked was something in its diet that it is getting now in silage."

This started another theory in Alfred's mind which was later substantiated by Dr. Chesnick of Columbus University: that the deep-rooted grasses and legumes are much higher in mineral content than surface grown cereal crops. Very often a cereal crop will be lacking in both nutritional and mineral content, whereas the deep-rooted grasses and legumes get mineral from the sub-soil. Tests had proven that the mineral content in grass silage runs about 6.3 pounds per ton dry matter basis. An animal can only assimilate 3.5 pounds per ton, which satisfies its mineral requirements, and the balance goes out in manure which in turn enriches the top soil. This, then, is what brought the pig back on its feet.

We closed the doors. All the stock, not so numerous this winter, was well cared for, warm, protected from the storm. We duck our heads down and, with shoulders braced, butt the storm, protecting Jim between us, as Alfred breaks trail anew up through the orchard past the snow-covered mound that is our new silo now covered with rails, straw and snow. With much stomping of feet to free our boots of snow before rushing quickly through the kitchen door to strip off barn clothing, our happy family, again complete, is ready to eat a special dinner to celebrate Alfred's safe return home. At special celebrations, like birthdays and today, when we are grateful no misfortune occurred we always eat our dinner in the living-room with candles, and whichever one is being honoured has his or her favourite food to make the occasion especially his or her own. Now it was time to hear all the details of the trip.

"I was halfway between Guelph and Kitchener. I'd gone twenty miles before I passed a car or saw any signs of traffic on the road, breaking trail all the way on rapidly closing in roads. I didn't go over thirty-five miles an hour all the way there and back, or attempt to pass anyone. When I got there, I told them I had to get home today because I had no one to look after things and I was worried about the state of the highways."

"We will get you through as quickly as we can,' they said.

"It took half an hour, and with a friendly, 'Good Luck' from them, I turned back, not even stopping for dinner. It was 11.30 a.m. when I left London. I ate the cookies you gave me on the road home."

"I wish I'd given you more."

"The roads got steadily worse. Around St. Mary's they were awful. People who tried to pass on the highway went straight off the road into the ditch. There were all kinds of cars abandoned along the way. I was never so glad to get home, out of that storm."

"And are we ever glad to have you safe home!" I sigh, contented and relaxed after my hard, gruelling day of worry, not work.

We were snowed in for three days. Alfred's was the last car down our road and another hour or so would have made it impossible for him.

"They told me when my appointment fell on a day as bad as this not to worry, just write and have it changed."

"Thank goodness for that."

Snug in our island in the snow, we are not entirely dependent on electricity. The old lamps in use again, we settle down to contemplate our future and the things we have learned, particularly in the past two years, that have added such excitement to our farming. We spend many long deliciously comfortable hours sitting by the friendly old stove I'd bought to serve till we could get a nice new shiny one to replace it. It rarely went out, and kept us snugly warm downstairs as well as heating Jim's room above so he could play with his toys in comfort. We felt a great depth of friendship for these old relics that contributed so nobly to our comfort. With just three hours necessary to do all the chores, Alfred had many pleasant hours to stretch his long legs beside the stove, reading about soils from countless sources, one of the best being the Journal of Soil and Water Conservation, published bi-monthly by the Soil Conservation Society of America, of which Alfred was now an associate member.

After New Year's, our stored-up restless energy was directed to the decorating that simply had to be done. The blue water-paint on the living-room ceiling, now flaking so much we were sure it would fall off, was to be replaced by oil paint. It all looked so delightfully easy. We'd strip off the wall paper and paint the walls too. We started. The chipped, peeling water-paint fought us to the last inch. It took an hour to clean a square foot of ceiling. We had started in the dining-alcove, a little room separated by a wide archway from the main living-room, and in reality a part of it. However, the wallpaper came off easily for a change. Everyone I'd asked what colour to paint the living-room had said green. I'd say, "What about pink?"

"Oh, no." They'd throw up their hands in horror. I still liked the thought of pink, and looked questioningly at Alfred. He came home from town with the pink paint.

There was only one way to find out. We started with the dining alcove, and painted it coral rose, finishing about two a.m. the night before a group of officials from V.L.A. were to come for noon dinner.

We seemed to have a faculty for starting something too big to finish with ease, just when we would want everything to look at its best. At least, it took any monotony out of these visits. If the farm programme was full of surprises, so too was the decor of the house.

The dinner was accompanied by interesting conversation, and, as was our practice on such occasions, everyone stayed at his own place at the table without any confusion of having dishes cleared away to interfere with the talk. Thoughts, ideas, facts, and questions were tossed amongst them like a ball in constant motion. Time passed quickly. The men, as always, must visit the barn before they went, though it was long past the hour they had planned on being somewhere else. One doesn't leave Friendship Farm in too great a hurry.

That over, we decided just for once to take our time with the rest of the room and enjoy the work rather than drive ourselves to be finished. We knew we liked the coral rose. Our little dining-alcove was lovely; warm, bright and friendly. We started in to clean the ceiling, turning it into a blotchy cracked white mess, and the red congoleum on the floor a motley sky blue with the scrapings. At ten p.m., exhausted, lolling in anything that looked comfortable, we pondered our task and decided to quit for the night.

Daisy telephoned just as sleepiness was taking possession of our lull.

"Anything doing this weekend? May I come up?"

"Sure, we'd love to have you."

"I'll come to Guelph Friday night."

"Alfred will meet you there."

"Fine."

I hung up. Alfred already was sloshing water on the walls. That was Tuesday. By Friday, the walls and ceiling were painted. We had only a door and one window left to do. The room, though unfinished, was no longer the undressed, ugly place we'd worked so hard in, and had enough of its new garment on to look decent and show what it would eventually look like.

We were just as ready to relax as our busy, hardworking friend who came to visit us. After dinner each night, Jim fast asleep in bed, Daisy and Alfred would get out the cribbage board and I would place my chair with the excuse that I wanted to be near the stove and have the light falling correctly over my left shoulder. In reality, I'd have my back to them and be able to indulge in a little catnapping. Lulled by the voices behind me, "—15-2, 15-15—" trying to hold my head up, each time it fell I'd waken with a start, remember my guest, and make some comment to assure them I was there, very interested and wide awake—fooling no one but myself.

The living-room was finally completed. The friends who threw up their hands in horror at the suggestion of pink, liked our coral rose. One, forgetting her advice, emphatically said, "I'm so glad you didn't paint it green."

Alfred called the trucker to come for the pigs, now ready for market. He came January 14, one day earlier than the date Alfred had written opposite the purchase date and price of the pigs. When the driver, from long experience a good judge of weights, saw the pigs, he said:

"They need another two or three weeks before they will be heavy enough for a good grade. I just watched pigs being weighed at a neighbour's of yours and they averaged 205 lbs. and looked much bigger than yours."

"His are all grain fed, fat and pot bellied. Mine are lean, all meat. They'll be heavy enough. Take them and we'll see."

The driver was surprised, when he had to give a little assistance to get one in the truck, at how heavy it really was.

When the sales slip returned with the cheque, all but one pig graded "A" Select. That one was a B, one pound underweight, which did not surprise Alfred half as much as the grading gratified him. He had known one to be not quite as big as the others, but had not wanted to hold it back alone. Pigs need company to do well. The weights averaged from 143 to 165 lbs. dressed. The best grade we had ever had was received from the thriftiest pigs we'd ever fed, and the feeding at half the previous cost.

We saw hog production in a larger way as an even more profitable enterprise than we had dreamed possible. The value of silage in farm economics could not be disputed, nor could any other known feeding method replace it.

When cashing the pig cheque, Alfred told a friend of his happy discovery. Realizing its importance, the friend remarked, "You won't tell anyone about it, will you?"

"Why not, if it will do any good?"

"Well, it might influence prices, and you wouldn't get the nice profit you do."

"I'll take that chance, if it will help a farmer keep his pork programme on the right side of his ledger."

"Crazy Leatherbarrow! He has a good thing and doesn't know enough to keep it to himself," thought our friend, "Destroying the goose that laid the golden egg."

The convention of the V.L.A. supervisors and field men drew near, Alfred would have liked so much to attend. We wondered what day the director would come and what he would be like. The days of that week came and went, and by Friday we had decided that the visit had been passed up. At noon, the call came.

"We would like to spend an hour on your farm this afternoon if it's convenient."

"Certainly."

It was almost four p.m. when they arrived. They set out immediately for the barn, where Alfred was doing the feeding. Here a lively discussion commenced as they examined the excellently preserved silage and listened to Alfred tell of how he was feeding it to poultry and swine with remarkable results. Finally, cold from standing round in the open pit, they all came to the house where I served tea and cookies, to continue an animated discussion. When Alfred found a mind worth picking, he never lost the opportunity to get all the information he could in the time at his disposal. Mr. Rutherford was keen, and a friendship was formed.

"Would you like to come down to the convention tomorrow? It's the last day to be spent in resumé of the week's discussions. You might find it interesting."

"I'd like to, but I don't think I'd better."

"Certainly," I chipped in. "Of course, he'll go."

I knew Alfred had wanted to attend the entire conference, but he had been assured it was for the staff only.

"Come tomorrow morning. I think you'll find it interesting," Mr. Rutherford repeated.

Alfred smiled, noncommittal. I'd have the fun of persuading him to go. It wouldn't be hard. He was halfway there already, I knew, because he liked this direct clear-thinking man he'd talked to for a few hours today.

Alfred got the chores done early, and all dressed up, as unlike the typical farmer as he could possibly be, set out for Guelph—and the surprise of his life.

Entering a hall filled with men, few of whom he knew, Alfred sought a seat at the back; but he had not escaped the notice of Mr. Rutherford on the platform. The latter whispered to the chairman; and he, after a few minutes discussion, came down and asked Alfred if he would address the meeting.

"What do you want me to talk about?"

"Just what you have done on your farm, how you started, on through."

Alfred took a long breath and commenced. For half an hour he told our story, and for nearly an hour answered questions from the floor.

On Tuesday, our first press notice appeared in the Guelph Mercury. The largest headlines on the second page introduced a well written review of Alfred's achievements.

Of course, we were delighted. Who wouldn't be, to receive recognition, unsought, not even desired, for work deemed worthy of notice by men engaged in improving the practice of agriculture on our Canadian farms? What new surprises were in store for us, we wondered.

Alfred told me as he recounted the surprising developments of that day, that at the end of his talk the chairman, after thanking him, held up a large sheaf of papers and said:

"These papers hold our programme for the coming year. We think we are up-to-date, but, as you have just heard, Mr. Leatherbarrow has been carrying out this programme for the past three years."

When Alfred arrived home that night his face was gleaming as he quietly said: "I have had my shining hour. If I don't have another, I'm well satisfied." Little did he know that it was just the beginning.

Thus a new era in farming, or rather of recognition for his farm practices, began for Alfred. From one day to the next, we never knew what was going to happen.

Mr. Way, the reporter who wrote the article for the Guelph paper, having called Alfred to his table before he left for substantiation of some of the amazing facts he had related, asked if he could quote these figures, fearful, no doubt, that they had been an exaggeration.

Mr. Way told Alfred that he would doubtless hear from other publications. A few days later a call came in from Toronto.

"This is Lex Schrag of the Globe and Mail," said the voice. "Gordon Way told me about the interesting work you are doing. Could I come up for an interview?"

"Sure."

A date was set. Like two kids, we just giggled. This was a game or a dream, but certainly not reality. People were not really interested in what we were doing here, on our out-of-the-way farm, on such a small scale that we didn't even come into an income tax bracket!

In honour of this auspicious occasion and to give it due respect, I rushed about to be sure all was tidy, dusted and neat, with my hair in pin curls intending to comb a nearly grown out permanent at the last moment. I stood washing dinner dishes by the window where one day we planned to have the sink with running hot and cold water. The man was to arrive about two p.m. and it was only one. I had lots of time; or did I? Mr. Schrag just then walked past the window, and Alfred was gathering eggs at the barn.

It was a dreary, cold, grey March day. A friendliness developed rapidly among the three of us as we talked. Finally it came time for our interviewer to take his leave. "I'd like some pictures, if I may have them, of the two of you here in the living-room," he said.

"Then, let me finish what you interrupted by arriving earlier than we expected," I asked, and hurried upstairs to change my dress and arrange my hair.

He posed us looking over our accounts, that being the key point of his article; and rightly so, for the ledger of necessity had always been the final arbiter of what we did or did not do. The only pencil beyond Alfred's famous little inch-long stub was one that had never been sharpened, so the article headlined "Farming The Easy Way Brings Excellent Profit," and the caption under our picture, "A sharp pencil!" appeared in the Globe and Mail, March 17, 1952.

This brought interesting correspondence which, in that first year, we endeavoured to answer; and there were visitors. I wish I'd kept a diary, or at least a visitor's book, but we were too busy with the surprises of each day, and our daily tasks, to keep track of much besides the general picture that was taking shape of an economic goal, that had seemed so far off, now being arrived at.

Taking stock, like any good businessman, we had things to think about, problems too, sober plans to make; and Alfred spent many sleepless hours at just this task. He figured that, now the productivity of the soil had been increased to such an extent, it would be wasteful not to increase the herd of cattle, already double the number we had not been able to feed the first year on the farm because of the low fertility of the soil. Alfred now had to do what any good businessman will do when he finds himself in the same situation, with a healthy production business and not enough capital.

Although we had chosen farming as a way of life and a hobby, it was also our living, and we had kept it on a strictly business basis from the beginning. Strict accounts governed all our operations. How well I remembered selling the laying flock because it proved unthrifty and we would soon be in the red if we kept them.

When you put farming on a business basis, you have no trouble in interesting sources of capital in your enterprise. Alfred had figured what he required for necessary expenditures in order to utilize to the full the good productive soil we now had, with the added advantage of economical farming methods. In seeking capital he was not begging for help. He was selling a good investment in a sound agricultural programme. We couldn't afford to gamble. It was not until now that Alfred was sure more capital would be a good risk, and the wisest method of utilizing to the full the capacity of our production. We needed capital to keep production in constant balance through crop yield and livestock consumption. Nothing being wasted, our economic position would be kept at a high level by complete utilization of our natural resources and low cost of production.

CHAPTER 15

Our first visitor since the publicity had catapulted us and our method of doing things into the public eye was a Scotchman. He was tall. He even towered over Alfred, who is six-feet-one. He was a mechanical engineer, working for a Texas firm and living in Ontario. His accent reflected this linguistic background as he talked.

"I drove past here looking for the place. I thought this might be it, seeing the ground covered, but I went on and asked a man working in his field up the road where the Leatherbarrow ranch was."

We gasped, "Ranch!" Our hundred acres! He continued.

"I want to buy a farm near Toronto to live on. I don't know much about farming, but you do. Now, when I find a place I like, if you will come and plan the cultivation of it, I'll pay you consultant fees, the same as I get in my business. A hundred dollars a day."

He had come and gone. We had taken time out for tea, yet the visit left us breathless and speechless, as though a big wind had suddenly swept us up and away, dropping us in a new and rosy world with sugar plums dangling all over the place.

Then there were the letters—fan mail—asking Alfred questions about farming and how to make more money. We, who up till now had had difficulty keeping up a subscription to a daily paper, often letting it lapse, enjoying the free service till it too would be cut off, then scraping enough "Doings" together to pay for three more months or possibly six, if we felt affluent. The height of luxury to us would have been to send our remittance for a whole year's subscription the moment it came due.

With that all past now, we felt a little like Cinderella, unaccustomed to the relaxing of the pressure of being unable, with insufficient capital, to do the things we wanted to do. We were really busy now; all the long hours of accurate figuring, and selling ideas, paid off with confidence and supported by the interest of important people in the business world.

Alfred set about streamlining our livestock enterprise to meet the increased production of his soil programme. He knew exactly what he wanted to do; the type of farming he liked and his own ability to carry through with the work. There is no point in attempting something you are not physically capable of accomplishing. A healthy individual is one who, recognizing this handicap, accepts it and works according to his ability, not forcing himself to do what is impossible, just because he'd like to be able to do it. We had been farming long enough to recognize our limitations. We also knew what branch of farming we liked best. With all these factors in mind, our planning took shape around them.

Having found the capital needed and an interested investor in our enterprise, everything was set for a streamlined programme to go into effect. Alfred had at last arrived at the beginning of a most interesting career in farming, with all the equipment and backing he needed to go right ahead. The old run-down farm had been given life-sustaining care over a period of years; understanding and a tenderness it sorely needed. Now, as it was coming into its own, it received a blood transfusion of capital, to bring it to its full stature.

How is it possible for us to feel other than humble and proud in being actively involved in this transition, aware of an unlimited Power with Whom it is our privilege to study and work?

At the beginning of our farm life, we had a dream of quiet peacefulness that did not exist amongst the hardworking farmers who could not break from tradition. Here in the country were slums, struggling against overpowering odds, men and women with few pleasures and little energy or time for them. If the market was good, they made a little extra, but the chances of much profit were slim. Weather hazards took care of that.

The average farmer is a fatalist. No wonder his sons run to the city. Few farmers consider it necessary to pay the son wages, even if they can. He gets his keep and the farm will be his eventually. In the meantime, a new suit of clothes, a little spending money, the car for an evening, is all he gets. He is a chattel, different from the other boys he meets in town and growing more and more aware of this difference, till finally he rebels. What was good enough for father and grandfather is not good enough for the son; and thank God this is so. The "old people", finding the farm-work too heavy alone, will have to adjust to new ideas, new methods, and find an honourable place on the land for their sons as men of intelligence and worth. We were the last ones on our concession to get a tractor, the last to get electricity, and the last to get a bathroom, but there are many farms without them still.

There was no luck in our success story. It was pluck and common sense. It was looking at farming as a business, not allowing the unexpected, which too often spells catastrophe, to swamp us, but rather finding out its cause and seeing it doesn't happen again. There is an element of surprise, no hum-drum monotony, even in doing the dinner dishes, when you have a lovely view from the window to look upon. Perhaps someone left a garden gate open and a big brood sow or Perry the boar crosses your vision, on the wrong side of the fence. Then you are off again, at your slimming exercises, before the cherished flowers are all rooted up.

There was a time when, driving through the country, this city gal thought, "How strange so few farm homes have masses of flowers with all the garden space they have."

It is true there are many more now, but I can understand why that was. There wasn't the water supply for one thing, with a hose that could be turned on so conveniently, or the time to look after them. A vegetable garden came first. It was practical.

Alfred made me a flower garden just where I could look at it from the kitchen window, and here I learned to dig my fingers into the soil, my thumb getting greener each year as my interest in gardening increased. We had transplanted the sixty living raspberry canes from the plot we expected a thousand to flourish on, also two rows of strawberry plants. These would not be allowed to bear fruit their first year, according to the best authority. I tended them with loving care and a watering mouth for the delicious fruit, my favourite; weeding, snipping the blossoms, watching them grow into healthy plants, directing the runners along straight rows. I was very proud of my strawberries. Then a long dry summer commenced, and I carried pail after pail of water to the plants. One by one they withered and dried. I had worked so hard keeping them clean that there was no mulch to hold the water when I gave it to them, or the rain when it came. So, we bought new plants and set them out in another section near the asparagus bed. This was before Alfred realized that the silo would have to be made larger. In the spring, the plants were big and healthy. We would have a wonderful crop. I didn't take the straw they had been covered with away, but packed it round the plants to hold the moisture and help retard the weeds. Each plant was covered with blossoms when Mack Neilson came to dig the silo.

"Watch out for my berries," I called.

"You bet. I'm coming back for a feed of them."

"That's fine. I'll make you a strawberry shortcake."

He kept his word, and terrified me by turning so short each time he came out of the silo with a scoop of earth. I put up stakes with binder twine to make it easier to see the space he had to work in, sure he didn't need to cut as sharply. Nothing happened, however, and the "electric fence" protected my garden patch from the countless feet of curious farmers who came to look at the first trench silo in our district and ask questions. The following year Alfred enlarged the silo, lengthening it another fifteen feet. When the plants were loaded with berries, Perry came with his men and a big cement mixer to pour sides for the silo, now formed for the purpose. It was to be made permanent. I warned them all to be careful of my berries and they assured me they would. They were. No one walked over them. All they did was shake each empty cement bag the way the wind was blowing so it wouldn't blow back in their faces. It was a westerly wind and carried the cement dust to lodge on my strawberries. We didn't have a ripe berry. We were better able to afford to buy the fruit this year, and I had refrigeration to keep them, so we just prepared another bed for new plants, and next year I'm sure I'll have lovely strawberries for our morning cereal and shortcakes.

The raspberries are in a safe location and they would soon be ready. Alfred's favourite. I was well content to slip out early, before breakfast to pick the first ones for his cereal.

With a man employed full time, for our son is not old enough to become a partner with his dad, as well as a number of workmen, carpenters, bricklayers, helpers swarming over the house and barn, I was busy getting meals for a few of them, fortunately not all, as well as looking after the baby chicks and the garden.

The blitzed fifteen-acre field in the spring was spread with manure direct from the stable, one-way disced once, cultivated once, and sown to a grass and legume mixture (brome, orchard grass, alfalfa, red clover and timothy) with a nurse crop of oats, one bushel to the acre, and the new land with fall wheat. All the rest of the farm was now in grass and legumes, and everywhere it promised a bounteous crop. The first cutting was to be ensiled; the second put in as dry hay, harvested during a season that is generally dry and sunny. Working with the advice of the weather bureau in mind, there would not likely be any spoiled hay this year.

Alfred doesn't race to be first man on the land. He waits till the ground is dry and workable, spreading the manure while others are seeding the grain fields. All around were showing green when ours was being seeded. The hired man was terribly worried, urging Alfred to get started when he saw how nice a neighbour's field looked, a green carpet against the blue spring sky.

"Don't worry. I know what I'm doing. When the land is ready, I'll start. You judge a crop by the harvest, not by what it looks like in the spring."

Sowing only one bushel of oats to the acre didn't please our young man, who wanted to be proud of the farmer he was working for and, perchance, boast a little when he met his friends at the Saturday night dances. This looked bad, and he was forced to keep silent and watch, no doubt thinking over the criticisms he'd often heard before he came to work for us. He shook his head and went about his work. . . . According to practices he was accustomed to, more than one bushel to the acre was generally sown as a nurse crop.

"It will stool out, you'll see, and the new seed won't get choked out either," Alfred told him.

A pig pen was being built of cement block by my brother Perry, designed by Alfred from ideas he'd been collecting ever since we started farming and knew he would like to keep brood sows. While the workmen poured the foundation for the new building that would complete an L-shape from the old pig pens,

Alfred and his helper tore out all the old pens, stripping the
building completely, ready to have a new cement floor and the
walls plastered. It, too, would be like a new building, for here
were to be the four new farrowing pens with their little retreats
where heat lamps would hang to give the new pigs warmth. The
right side housed the farrowing pens. On the left, one large pen
ran from one end to the outside wall of the new wing. Here was
an exit for pigs only, to come and go as they desired, for they
would be the ones waiting to farrow. I call them ladies-in-wait-
ing. A feed alley runs between these pens to a door that can only
be opened from the inside. A scale is near it for weighing purposes, convenient and handy in the exit alley.

In the new building, a centre alley for feeding all the
troughs filled simply, unhindered by over-anxious snouts
nosing about. At the back of the pens, all of which are of cement
block, is an alley for cleaning purposes with doors that do
double duty, closing off pens as desired and leaving the alley
open its full length, or as much as is desired. The litter-carrier
I'd wheedled Alfred into installing, now unnecessary in the stable, was installed here, running down each cleaning alley and
the length of the large pen; exit doors only at the end of each
alley permit no admission except through one door that is kept
locked. This permits no visitors without the attendance of
Alfred or his herdsman, and with disinfectant pans impossible
to avoid, the utmost precautions against disease are observed.
When the pig pen was completed one rainy day, Alfred collected all the odd cans of paint about the place and, mixing
everything together, he and his helper proceeded to paint the
doors. The colour turned out to be a nice fuschia, and we immediately named the building "Perry's Pink Pig Palace."

Although Perry was not always present when his men were
working on the building, Alfred, knowing exactly what he
wanted, became known to the workmen as "the architect", for
very often their interpretation of what was right had been
wrong and Alfred showed them the correct way. He'd given too
much thought and planning to this project not to know exactly
how each detail should be carried out. A 30 foot by 40 foot and
32 foot by 75 foot L-shaped, completely new pig pen was ready
to receive disease-free breeding stock. Our next move was to
purchase the breeding stock, nine gilts, five bred and four open,

and a boar. English large white Yorkshire pure bred registered stock formed the nucleus of our new breeding enterprise. They would rattle around more or less in the new building, but it would not be long before it would be filled.

The section over the old pig pen was already a chicken house. This was carried through to the outside wall of the new building. The remaining section of the L was to be a straw loft for the pig pens. Thus, we were able to increase our laying flock, with additional space where the old granary had been, the adjoining section carrying it to the wall. We could house up to 1,500 laying hens. A carpenter made us six range shelters large enough to house 250 pullets each.

When the pasture land was about ready and Alfred calculated how many cattle he could carry without over-pasturing, we set out to purchase the nucleus of a beef herd. Shopping around, Alfred finally purchased ten bred heifers, good grade Herefords with the lot of twenty-three we had and about the same weight. The farm looked quite different from previous years when grades of all breeds and few in number roamed over our poor pastureland.

Standing on the brow of the hill near the gravel pit looking at the uniform lot, all with shiny red brown coats, white spots on most of them and white faces, we picked this breed for their beauty as well as beef qualities in mind, unable in anything to be completely mercenary.

"In the fall, I'll get a good registered bull," Alfred said. "We will keep the right heifers from the lot of thirty-three. That will give us a good start raising our own cattle, and we can increase it as the soil can carry the increased number. There is plenty of pasture this year, without any over-grazing."

After having to part with pets whom we had named with personal tenderness for friends and relations, we were determined to be cold-blooded about these heifers. However, it was quite natural that in walking through the herd, scratching behind the ears of any that would allow it, Alfred should soon have at least one devoted friend. She was a motley brown and white, perhaps the least attractive from a colour point of view in the whole herd. She belonged to the group of twenty-three feeders Alfred had carried over the previous winter and, in the barn, had manoeuvred for more than her share of scratching.

Whenever Alfred entered the field she would appear at his elbow and be duly scratched. It wasn't long before she had a name—Margaret. She stood out amongst the others, who looked as if they were in formal dress, all being uniform in colour and markings, with their white feet, faces and vests. I wonder if she knew that Alfred had planned on letting her go when he sold the steers, and she was wheedling her way into his affections, for stay she did.

There was so much growth on this fourteen-acre field allotted to summer pasture that the cattle, thirty-three head from May 1st to September 1st, were not able to handle it at all, and Alfred later cut four acres for dry hay because it was getting ahead of them. This was the field which he had been thought wrong to manure immediately prior to seeding down. It was proof again of the value of unleached manure worked into, not under, in the spring just before seeding. In spite of this, the boy we had working for us still thought Alfred all wrong when he took time to manure the blitzed field in the spring before seeding, when everyone else had finished their seeding, and a lot of it was already showing green on the fields. We had proof in our fields, but were still alone in practice.

We now had our livestock programme started. I went with Alfred in Perry's truck the day we picked up the pigs. It was a lovely day, and a happy one, fulfilling one of his ambitions to have good breeding stock.

"I'll keep everybody out of the pens, in fact never allow anyone in the pig pen unattended," he said. "I don't want any rhinitis in this stock."

It was going to remind me of a hospital ward, clean, disinfectant always evident, little pigs, the prettiest, most fascinating to watch of all the stock, to keep me visiting the pens frequently. My nursing even came in handy, for I'm sure had I not had it I would have been terrified to drive a needle through thick pig skin, or watch a restless sow about to farrow. I used to hold the little pigs while Alfred did the necessary surgery to make them barrows. Now he had a man to assist with that.

At the same time, the men were digging a ditch through the orchard from the barn, and five others were fanning across the lawn, which was no more. The house was like a fortress, secure behind a series of moats, formidable in dry or wet weather. In the house we had beds to sleep on though it was often difficult to reach them, and when they installed a double sink with metal cupboards on either side, under the south kitchen window, I was allowed the privacy of that corner to prepare meals. The rest of the house belonged for the time being to the workmen. Carpenters were tearing down walls and building new ones. The old ghost walk and small bedroom were no more. In their place, we had a larger bedroom, small hallway, clothes closet off the bedroom, linen room off the larger hall and a bathroom, the most beautiful room in the house, planned for six years ago, and now far more wonderful than I had ever dreamed possible. Blue congowall to cover the cracked plaster of old walls, with chrome to seal the corners, white fixtures, a counter sink, and a tricky arrangement of mirrors, on the wall and gable behind, to enable me to sit at my dressing table and see the back of my head without the use of a hand mirror. Hot and cold water on tap all the time. It was too good to be true, yet it was true.

After the bathroom had been planned, the problem of what to do about the stove we had set up in the living-room in winter, that also heated this section of the upstairs, was quickly settled by Alfred.

"I saw the bathtub would cover the stovepipe hole, so there was nothing for it but to put in a furnace."

It was ordered, and the men were busy in the cellar, tunnelling under the kitchen where there was no cellar, up and down stairs, in the pantry, under the stairs. Workmen swarmed over the entire house and I worked at getting meals like a sleep walker, dreaming such beautiful dreams I hated to wake up. It was all real. They were finally gone.

I wanted the colour in the new bedroom to be warm and friendly. It was to be used by a hired man, and as it was a north room, I chose a golden yellow paint for the walls with an orange red for the furniture. The walls turned out to be orange. They were terrible. A second coat of almost ivory produced the desired shade, soft and glowing. One could stay in the room without screaming. The old furniture painted red gave the warmth and welcome we desired, with frilly curtains, a radio and lamp. All we needed was another more comfortable chair, and that we'd look for at sales. Green floor covering completed the upstairs.

We were now living in the way we had been accustomed to, and for a long time had desired to be accustomed to again. No ashes to clean out, no fires to tend. Heat whenever I desired it and air-conditioning in the summer. We no longer sweltered upstairs in the summer and froze in the winter. I could bathe and dress leisurely, luxuriously, without shivering in the cold or scurrying into the house lest I be caught. This is the way people engaged in the most important industry of our civilized world should be able to live.

There had never been much grass around the house, though I tried nobly to have a lawn. A dry season would burn up the grass and only plantain grew, taking over with burdock if we allowed it. Tradesmen, junk dealers, city slickers all drove over the lawn as close to the door as possible, where with the same disrespect they leaned heavily on their horns, expecting a mild subservient farmer or his wife to appear. One such horn pusher could see from where he sat behind the wheel of his car Alfred's back through the kitchen window where he was eating his dinner. We didn't move. Alfred finished his dinner and set out for the barn. The occupant of the car hurriedly followed on foot. He was at a disadvantage from the beginning. A salesman wanting to interest Alfred in the minerals he sold.

"I wondered if you were paralyzed. I see you aren't."

"I wouldn't buy any from you even if I wanted some. A man who hasn't the decency to get out of his car and come to the door doesn't deserve to make a sale."

The man dismissed, Alfred proceeded to the barn.

All through our six years on the farm we received discourtesy that would not be attempted in town. Who would permit anyone to drive over his front lawn? We are proud, self-respecting people, and cannot tolerate such ignorant manners, and worst of all the encroachment on our privacy. I used to think a farm house, isolated, away from neighbouring houses, would be such a nice solitary place where one's privacy would never be interfered with. Yet here, hunters cross the fields as though they were their own. In six years a possible half dozen hunters have asked permission to hunt our land. Our son Jim has to run for the orchard where we hope he will be safe. Yet, who else has as much right to the freedom of our land? The dog never leaves the shed when hunters are around and our country is supposed to be at peace, and during the hunting season we roam our rolling land in danger of being shot. These are hazards in farming that have nothing to do with the farmer's occupation, but rather with the inconsiderate carelessness of the man to whom nothing but his own personal enjoyment is of any importance.

So, the ditches all over the lawn in 1952 gave us the protection we had often despaired of getting from any but the visiting farmers and people sincerely interested in our agricultural developments. We had a gate cutting off the driveway to the garage from the farm lane, a bother to us, so only shut when cattle were grazing in the pasture beyond.

There were a dozen cars lined up in the lane one day when the Fuller Brush man arrived.

"Is there a sale in progress?" he inquired.

"No, just visitors," I answered.

The Rawleigh man from whom I always bought our spices would stay awhile, always to talk farming and dream a little of farming himself.

CHAPTER 16

On a cold wet dismal day in late March, before workmen had started remodelling the house, we had a day of appointments made by mail by farmers who had read the article in the Globe and Mail, two from Acton, and five from Goderich. Two days earlier, Alfred had met a bread delivery man and asked him to commence calling on us twice a week. It was the day he was to call, and I had allowed our supply to dwindle to half a loaf of sliced bread. We aren't heavy bread eaters. It worried me not in the least. No one coming that day was expected to stay for meals.

The lads from Acton arrived early after dinner. Alfred took them through the barn, showed them the silo with the good silage, and how well the cattle did on it and hay alone. They came back to the living-room and talked farming, the most interesting topic of conversation in our home. It was nearly five. As they were leaving, five tired cold-looking men appeared.

"We were lost and have been all over the countryside looking for this farm."

"Come in! Come in where it is warm," we shouted.

Three veterans of the war of 1914-1918 and two from the second world war sat around our dining-room table and talked farming and feeding. Time passed so quickly. I sat with them, always an interested listener, casting hopeful glances toward the road, hoping to see the bread truck driving up the lane. These men looked tired and hungry, and I was low again on supplies.

By six I knew he wasn't coming, so I sharpened the bread knife and proceeded to slice each slice in half, making fried egg sandwiches and serving them with coffee and store cookies. I'm sure that never before had they seen such thin sandwiches, in spite of a whole egg in each one, or as flimsy. I told them of my predicament, and everyone laughed. It was all right, and they were off, deep in conversations on methods of cultivation. Time was forgotten till about eight o'clock, with a long trip home ahead of them and each with chores to do when he got home. One of the older men said:

"Well, laddie, you have just put us back in the pig business," and they were off.

"Isn't it wonderful talking to people like that? To think they'd come all this way too."

"It's good to be able to tell a person something he can profit by."

"I hope we will always be able to."

We will never forget those men and their visit with us. It occurred during a lull between the unexpected publicity, and the extensive remodelling and building our increased capital made possible. After that the countless visitors came and went daily, creating interesting pauses in a busy day.

In Guelph one day, at the V.L.A. office, Alfred was told that Mr. Rutherford had just sent word asking them to invite Alfred to go on a tour of Ohio farms with a group of V.L.A. officials, ending the tour at Malabar Farm.

"No, thank you very much, but when I go to Malabar Farm it will be with my wife."

Alfred was very definite about his refusal and when he told me, flattered and naturally pleased by his consideration, I tried to persuade him to call back and accept the invitation.

"No. That trip we take together."

He could not be persuaded to change his mind, so we forgot about it, each in his own way thinking often about how nice it would be.

It was now time to start filling the silo, and all was in readiness. Alfred liked to start filling on Saturday, letting it settle and have time to heat and start the ensiling process to insure a sweet silage. He learned from Dr. Weir that it was very important to let it start heating so that the heat would go right up through the silage. Otherwise, it would be a cold sour silage and therefore not as palatable. He also learned that it was wrong to exclude all the air immediately, because by excluding air bacteria action would be stopped. A little air is needed, but too much would be more harmful than none at all. Alfred figured that fifteen or twenty minutes tramping with the tractor each night would be sufficient to exclude enough air. He would fill all day, then pack for fifteen or twenty minutes each evening. When the silo was filled, he would pack each day for almost an hour, keeping this up for a week, then cover the silage with six inches of straw and earth and would have practically no spoilage.

During the summer, possibly once a week, the tractor would be run over this for about fifteen minutes to keep it packed and settled. He must have hit it just right, because for the past three years the silage has been beautiful and sweet-smelling. A 40-60 ratio of grasses and legumes, using grasses high in carbohydrate, aids in giving a good balanced fermentation. Alfred asked Dr. Weir about preservatives. He told him that, since Alfred had read and studied so much about grass silage, he didn't think using preservatives was necessary, explaining that if you put 3,000 lbs. of molasses on the silage you don't get the equivalent when feeding, because the bacteria have consumed one third of it.

Farmers asking about the smell of the silage were surprised when Alfred told them that, ensiled in a trench, there is not the same pressure as in a tower silo and therefore the silage is sweeter smelling and more palatable.

"No. My wife does not object. The odor is not carried into the house and when the silo is opened and she comes to the barn, she likes the pungent odor."

Filling the silo was to start this year on Monday; allowed to rest Tuesday; then filling continued till all was in. There were seven different mixtures in his fields, so that the one that was ready first being sixty per cent orchard grass, forty per cent alfalfa, the saturation point for protein of the predominating grass was the deciding factor as to which mixture should be harvested first. Here, the orchard grass predominating had just headed. It was ready. The alfalfa was just showing bloom. From this field they would go to one of alfalfa and brome grass. Here the alfalfa predominated. It would be at ten per cent bloom when they would reach it, just right for ensiling. From here to a field again predominating in alfalfa, with brome grass and Ladino. Next, alfalfa and timothy, about 50-50 ratio, with the timothy at saturation point, the heads just coming out of the shot leaf. Lastly the new seeding, with red clover predominating at about half bloom for saturation point.

Thus, Alfred could take his time, each crop being at saturation point when harvested; learning a lot with different mixtures in forage crops, and having no trouble getting each harvested when its predominating grass was at saturation point for protein, which is what he is growing it for.

Sunday morning routine is waffles for the first real meal of the day, anywhere between eleven a.m. and two p.m., according to when we had our fruit juice and coffee, and if everyone is up. A week-end guest is always allowed to sleep as long as he desires. The waffles and sausages were nicely finished and each one of us was deciding how we wished to spend the next hour or so of our leisurely Sunday afternoon when a car drove in. Three men emerged and walked, as always, to the silo.

"Alfred, it's Mr. Rutherford," I called excitedly up the stairs.

The quiet of our day was over. Alfred went out, talked with the men, and took them through the now completed and inhabited pig pen. Then, waiting for the men to come to the house, I decided on persuading Alfred, if there was still room in the car, to go on the tour. I could hardly contain myself till the men appeared and I was able to draw Mr. Rutherford aside and ask him if there was still time for Alfred to change his mind and go, and if so, to help me persuade him.

I got my opportunity but didn't know that Alfred had already turned down the invitation, repeated while touring the pig pens.

Standing in the field of orchard grass and alfalfa, Mr. Rutherford had said, "My, that's a wonderful crop."

"Yes, but it's not as good as last year. Then it was up to my nose. Come on over the hill and I'll show you something better," Alfred said.

He took them to a field of alfalfa, brome and Ladino that was up to Alfred's nose and the top of Mr. Rutherford's head. Mr. Rutherford turned to the other men and said, "I don't know about you chaps, but I haven't seen anything in Ontario that can compare with this, and I don't expect to see anything like it till we get to Bromfield's place."

When they got back to the house, old friends meeting again and in jovial mood, I nodded meaningfully to Mr. Rutherford, who quickly asked, "Won't you come with us, Alf?"

"Yes, do," from me. "We can manage splendidly. Hurry. Go and get dressed and I'll pack for you."

At last they were all away, and the place seemed dreadfully empty. I was up early next morning, waiting for our hired man to arrive. As he walked around the house, he was greeted with, "You are head man for the next five days. Alfred went to Ohio yesterday."

"What!" He grinned and pushed his cap farther back on his head as realization of what he had to do this week dawned on him.

"The silo. What about it?"

"You start filling today. If your brother isn't needed at home, get him to help you. You know exactly what to do; what to cut first; everything. Just carry on."

"Holy gee!" Our young farmer, capable and strong, strode down through the orchard to feed the pigs, and to take over in full charge at this important time. He called his home and his brother came over. It was fun to watch them. The older boy was the big boss now, responsible, and carrying it well. I had nothing to worry about. There were minor little mishaps, but nothing serious, and work proceeded as planned.

Wednesday, at suppertime, long distance called. It was Alfred. The gap was bridged, sunshine in our voices. We didn't need television to see it in our faces. It was close to midnight when a tired field man and his wife brought Alfred back, and stopped long enough for coffee and sandwiches, before going on another hundred miles or so, home. We talked on into the night, each with so much to tell the other, after Alfred had been assured that everything was in fine working order, and our helper had done a good job.

"Mr. Bromfield was away," said Alfred. "Some mistake in the arrangements. He expected us the day before, so I didn't feel so badly at not having you with me when he wasn't there. I was the only practising farmer and guest of the V.L.A., in a group of sixty officials on the tour. We visited a dairy farm, grass farm, poultry farm and the Experimental Station at Wooster, Ohio, where every animal on the place is on test for something. The last day was at Malabar Farm. On reaching one field of a grass legume mixture in process of being ensiled, I was standing by one of the supervisors from the London office, and he asked the farm manager whether, for this district, that crop was considered a good one.

"Oh yes," was the quick reply. "Quite good." After a pause, the supervisor turned to me and asked, "How does that compare with yours, Alf?'

"Feeling a little embarrassed, and not wanting to make my own comparisons, I said, 'I can't answer that question. Ask one of the men who visited my place last Sunday—that chap right there.'

"Calling him over, he asked, 'You saw Alf's crop on Sunday. How did it compare with this?'

"Alf's crop was much better. It was at least a foot higher, and thicker.'

"I turned and said, 'You see why I couldn't answer that question.' "

Later in the fall Mr. Rutherford had occasion to dine with us, and told us that he had written to thank Mr. Bromfield for the time the group spent on his farm, stating his regret that Mr. Bromfield was away at the time, as he had a farmer veteran with him who, that year, had produced crops more abundant than his own.

Sunday was beginning to be anything but a day of rest, though decidedly interesting. If we wanted our solitary walk around the fields, we had to go now in the early morning, for the afternoon brought guests, and Alfred would be talking farming all afternoon to anywhere from two to thirty interested farmers. This Sunday we found ourselves alone towards the end of the day, and I was going out to look at my perennial border when a car drove up and a friendly young woman walked up to me, saying, "I know. You are Margaret. I can tell from your picture."

I searched frantically in my memory for a mutual friend who might have a picture of me.

"In the Globe and Mail," she added.

From here a friendship was formed. Her husband, a veteran with a trucking business in Hamilton and a dream wish to farm, had come to us to talk about it. We had a picnic supper, our guests contributing their share, and ended a pleasant day with the assurance that our would-be farmer could come up week-ends to help a little and learn a lot.

The first Saturday morning he arrived the men worked at preparing the new chicken house in the old granary, more carpentry than farming, but our friend learned a lot about improvising. Alfred could scrounge around amongst his treasures and come up with the very hinge or bracket he needed, rather than dashing to town to swell the merchants' profits. The camaraderie, as they worked, relieved tensions our new friend felt as he battled the asphalt jungle all week on his trucking missions.

With things running smoothly, we decided that we could now take time out for a visit to Quebec, Alfred's childhood home. Leaving the hired man in charge, we tucked Jim in the back seat, road-map in hand to check off the towns through which we passed, and we were off.

As the grey of early morning started to lighten into a misty dawn along the river, we turned north at Dorion following a wooded highway through the French Canadian countryside that held nostalgic memories for both of us, to Como, a little village, old world and new, with white picket fences and nameplates on the gates-houses flush with the sidewalk—the shops, show-windows in dwelling houses, and all so cosy and friendly. Now it was very quiet. They were fast asleep, unaware of the beauty of the pink glow of sunrise behind the mist, rising from the lake, tree shadows like ghost figures emerging, taking shape as the colours deepened and the growing pink heralded the dawn for us. It was Alfred's first reunion with his family since we were married.

It was very pleasant, going back a success, with a growing flourishing business to return to. He had not seen his sisters for six years. They found it difficult to understand our success. This, their youngest, had been in farming so short a time and had tackled the profession with so little preparation.

On Sunday night we all went up to the little stone church nestled in the woods, brown and aged, where Alfred's brother-in-law was organist and choir leader. Service over, Bill sat at the organ and played each hymn we called for. The following day we visited our old haunts in and around Ste. Anne's. Then it was time to be on our way to Montreal. We didn't belong here any longer, and would, probably never return. The difference was in us. One last drive down the road where we had walked to our favourite picnic ground in the bush, and we were back on the highway, passing through the little towns that were now almost one with the city.

We didn't try to make the trip home without a stop, and, as night drew on, found a tourists' camp, and spent the night on the shores of Lake Ontario. As we had expected it would be, everything at home was in perfect order, under the conscientious care of our helper. By now he was assured that Alfred had been absolutely right in his treatment of the fifteen-acre field, where a beautiful crop of oats was running fifty bushels to the acre, in spite of having been sown at one bushel to the acre. Each seed had started out five and six shoots, growing to full maturity, with heavy heads of grain to harvest by combine; the harvester picking up and blowing the straw conveniently into the mow.

After the wheat had been combined, as was Alfred's custom now, the straw was disced in and oats were sown for pasture and cover, till seeding the next year. There would be nothing more to do in the fields other than clipping pastures to keep the weeds from maturing and reseeding themselves until the second hay crop would be taken in, and Alfred would be back from his second trip to Ohio long before that time.

The morning we left for Ohio with Mary Dass, we started at nine a.m. It was to be a leisurely trip. On his previous visit, Alfred had noted motels that were attractive, and we planned each day's distance accordingly.

The first night we spent in the mountains along the Allegheny trail. The second at Cochocton, where Mary would rest and read her favourite detective stories and Alfred would take me to the field day being held at the Hydrological station nearby.

We climbed onto a wagon, with baled hay in rows to seat the visitors, and toured the station listening with interest as each test plot we passed was explained and inspecting the Lysimeters, that provide data as close to nature as it is possible to attain. Back to our wagon again, in friendly conversation with a young couple, farmers from near Akron, Ohio, whom we would meet again in a group of six thousand two days later. From Cochocton, we went in to Wooster where a Dairy Day was being held and Alfred wanted to attend a movie and a lecture on nutrition. Here, through a window in a cow's side, digestion could be observed and different processes tested. It was here, talking with Dr. Chesnik, that Alfred was assured his theory in the breakdown of silage was correct.

Making our headquarters at a lovely motel in Wooster, we drove out to Malabar Farm. This time to meet and talk with Mr. Bromfield. We returned the following day to attend a Field Day sponsored by *Successful Farming Magazine* in pouring rain, in a crowd of six thousand, with my raincoat safe and dry in its little envelope back in the car. With an invitation to call in on the farm of our new acquaintances, we chose a different route home. We stopped there to drive around the dairy farm, see the hay drier and test plots and talk a while, going on to Buffalo, where we stayed the last night of our trip, dining in style and dancing.

We arrived home on August 11th, about mid-afternoon, much to our hired man's relief, for two sows were due and showing every sign of farrowing that night.

CHAPTER 17

At half past nine in the evening, two excited anxious people stood in the alley, looking at two sows in farrowing pens, next to one another. The lamps hanging over the creeps were turned on, making a golden glow in a corner of each pen. The clean fresh straw, piled high by the waiting sow for her bed, having been made over and over again as restlessness forced her to keep busy, would catch the light, reflecting ribbons of gold curling and twisting as the anxious mother-to-be nosed about to be sure all was snug and safe for her offspring. She was accustomed to Alfred. He was her friend, so when he entered the pen one could almost feel after her first apprehensive grunt that she was grateful to have him near in her hour. He talked to her quietly, soothingly. I stood by, tired and sleepy, yet wide awake, rooted to the spot, the miracle of birth filling me with the same awe and wonder, humility and peace, as I feel when watching a cow give birth to a calf. I felt pride in watching the gentle kindness of my husband as he arranged his equipment; pinchers to cut the baby's black teeth and a cloth to wipe it dry.

We waited. With each labour pain my husband, from the look I saw on his face, had one too, and before the night was out, both of us had as sore stomach muscles as the sows, who had good reason for theirs.

By one a.m., Alfred said, "I have an awful pain in my stomach."

"What is the matter?" I asked in alarm.

"I know what's the matter. Every time a sow pushes a pig out, I push one too. I never thought I'd get sympathy pains from a pig."

We laughed, knowing Alfred has to suffer on till the farrowing is complete. The little pigs, all pink and damp were like little helpless babies. Alfred took each one up quickly lest the mother, striking out with her feet in pain would injure it.

Deftly, painlessly he snipped the teeth, dried its little pink body then placed it safe in the creep with clean golden straw where the warmth of the heat lamp soothed its quivering body and it slept peacefully, waiting for its brothers and sisters, who would join it. As each pig was born and we recovered from our sympathy pain, our eyes would meet and we would smile triumphantly like conspirators who had accomplished a remarkable feat, keeping absolute silence so as not to disturb the mother suffering the pangs of birth. It was the Maple Leaf sow and she was quiet, and patient, with never a sound as she produced ten perfect little pigs.

How did we know they were all? It was not the fact that she arose, but rather that the moment her last baby was born, she called. Like the cow, the pig with all motherhood in her voice now called her young, and the peacefully sleeping babies awoke in an instant and, for the first time finding their wobbly feet, squealed and were impatient to find their way out of the creep which Alfred has closed off for training purposes. They have to wait while he lifts each one and gently places it near its mother. With unerring skill, they find the source of food supply and; with an energy that is almost unbelievable, fight for a place of vantage, squealing excitedly; then, finding the convenient nipple they suck noisily until satisfied. They fall asleep, wakening as the grip is lost, to pull again and again, and at last succumb completely to sleep. Back in the creep Alfred places each little pig, satisfied they have all had their fill and the mother is kind and gentle.

With another sow to come in tonight, it will not be the same trouble to return every hour to set the pigs out to nurse, which Alfred will do about three times. The last time he will remove the blocks from the creep holes, and the little pigs will find their mother under their own power; then, with unerring instinct they will return to the comfortable warmth of their creep, safe from harm in case the mother is careless and with her huge heavy body should crush one or step on it. It is well worth the extra time spent in putting the piglets out and back again several times till they are steadier on their feet and have learned where safety and warmth can be found.

Alfred looked exhausted and no wonder; labour pains ten times! We laugh at ourselves. It's silly, but that's us and we can't change much now.

"You rest. I'll watch the other and call you."

It is close to midnight. Alfred had just finished arranging a pallet of burlap bags to rest on when I called, "Here's one."

Quietly he entered the pen and spoke gently to the apprehensive sow, who as quickly relaxed, giving full attention to her own troubles now. The same procedure as before continued till four-thirty in the morning, and perhaps because it was also my birthday, the sow we named Margaret had given birth to nineteen beautiful little pigs.

Until they are weaned at eight weeks old, when some weigh as much as sixty-six lbs., the mother, with the same mother tones, will call her young to be fed and they will as they grow larger swarm all over her, nuzzle her nose, until I'm sure they are kissing one another. When they are older and mother feels they've had enough, she'll turn gently until she is lying on her breasts and they can't reach them or wheedle her into another sip. Here in the pig pen there is firmness and authority, gentleness and love, intelligence, patience and gratitude, with quirks of temperament common to the human race.

Four of Margaret's little boars were marked and put immediately on the Maple Leaf sow so the lunch counters could supply them all. Of the twenty-nine pigs born that night, two were lost. When the four pigs were marked, they and the litter of ten were all dubbed with a bit of oil so they would all smell alike, otherwise a quiet motherly sow would have become a killer and snapped the four to death so quickly they could not have been saved.

Watching Alfred handle the pigs so gently and efficiently, I thought of when he had told me his ambition as a boy had been to be a surgeon, and knew had he had the opportunity he would have been a good one. Long, slender sensitive fingers, working steadily, carefully and with sureness. I thought also, was he not now contributing as much to the welfare of the human race as he would have in the profession of his boyhood dreams?

Now, with the opportunity, and using it, he was starting a breeding herd of pigs from the best stock he could buy in Canada. I remembered a remark of Herb's, "Anyone can do well. To be really good you have to be at least five per cent better than the average."

Our breeding stock had to be above average. Up till now, Canadian Yorkshire, or Tamworth. All the pigs we had bought, and some for breeding purposes, had not come up to the standard desired by Alfred, nor had they been as thrifty, usually not as vigorous or hardy, taking up to seven months to feed to market weight, which lowered the percentage of the farmer's profit until it very often didn't exist.

The English Large White Yorkshire breed we purchased had all the attributes we desired, and, with a pig-pen worthy of their occupancy, we were justly proud of this branch of our farm enterprise.

Strict cleanliness observed, with only one entrance, kept locked, no one could enter without an attendant. Disinfectant pans outside and inside this door. Signs placed so that they would have to be read, refusing admittance to any pen, and demanding that feet be kept off trough fronts. It would be impossible for the most uncouth to disrespect our demands. The alleys were kept free of debris, and amazed visitors would exclaim, "Why, they are clean, and it smells nice in here."

It makes me think of a hospital ward when I walk down the alleys at night and see the sows clean and comfortable in their beds of clean straw, snug against one another. Or, if it is a warm night, lying off, apart, but so comfortable, clean and dry. It is their breathing that makes me think of patients in wards, asleep. I find myself walking on tiptoe, lest they be disturbed. With the smell of disinfectants, if I close my eyes, a vapoury picture recalling years of night duty and rounds made in dimly lit wards is superimposed, and, opening my eyes again, I am startled and relieved to be back in this reality, this absorbing, interesting work with its variety that embraces agriculture practised the world over. Alfred knows each sow by now, though they all look alike to me. Even when it is asleep he will point one out and tell me some little story about its habits and temperament.

They do not bring to our minds their market value only, but rather the establishment of a breeding herd of which only the very best will be kept for breeding purposes or sold for breeding stock. We realize that they could be sold as breeding stock for a very high premium, but we want to see other farmers get ahead as we are doing. Therefore, our breeding stock for sale is priced so little over the market price that farmers can buy them to improve their stock. A set scale of prices, reasonable and fair, the same for all buyers, gives us a reasonable profit and a good sense of well-being and fellowship with our fellow man.

Alfred has worked towards taking the risk out of raising pigs by using sensible precautions. During the hog cholera epidemic he put screens on all the windows, keeping the pigs inside all the time, clean as usual. Visitors were discouraged by placing a sign on our gatepost, "Absolutely no visitors during Hog Cholera Epidemic." It was respected and we are grateful.

Watching through that dreadful scare was nerve-racking indeed, never knowing when the day would come that, entering the pig pen, we would find some beautiful sow suffering from the dread disease. It passed us by and we are grateful, but continue ever watchful.

Time spent by Alfred in the pens, having the pigs get to know him, scratching their heads behind the ears as they nose one another out for first chance, helps keep them quiet, relaxed and growing. Like humans, pigs can become nervous, irritable and bad-tempered. Kindness and affection bring as rapid response from a pig as from a lonely individual. When Perry, our boar, arrived, some time after the sows, Alfred scratched his head before he even uncrated him, nervous at being shipped and pushed about. Every day, in the special pen with extra high sides, Alfred scratched his head and talked to him till the animal would sink slowly to his knees and with all the expressions of delight look up pleading for more. When Perry grew big and strong, weighing some eight hundred pounds, with mighty tusks to terrify the most rugged, he would still look pleading for more, into Alfred's face and grunt a gentle insistence, standing perfectly still as long as Alfred scratched. Alfred quite enjoys putting on this little show for visitors, particularly the non-farming type who are so amazed at what they see here anyway.

We like to be present at every birth, particularly if it is a first litter, for the sow may have personality traits that are dangerous to her litter. One such sow, daughter of a perfect mother, snapped two of her newborn litter in two so rapidly that there was barely time to rush the remainder to safety. Repeatedly Alfred tried to persuade her to take her offspring, but each time she snapped her refusal.

This lovely sow with all the attributes but one required for our breeding stock, signed her own death sentence with her ugly nature. There was no other litter born at the same time, whose mother, if she had enough teats, could take this nice litter rejected by its own mother. Alfred hurried to town, bought nursing bottles and nipples and a formula from a veterinary surgeon. Fixing up an orange crate with clean straw, he brought the litter to the kitchen. Here, every two hours day and night we fed the piglets, a poor substitute for a good mother; and only the hardiest survived, three out of nine, two of whom the mother had killed. At night setting an alarm clock we took turns to go downstairs, warm the formula and feed the pigs every two hours. As they grew older their healthy voices were better than an alarm clock, and as insistent as babies' crying. At the end of a week, with us weary and suffering from loss of sleep, they were transferred to a creep. Here, every four hours, I took them warm formula. We were training them to sip from a dish.

Never again will we try to save a litter rejected by the mother. No matter how clean we kept our charges in the kitchen, they had a distinct odour all their own, unnoticed in the pig pen but foreign to our kitchen. There is, however, always a first time for everything and an experience worth having.

The mother—we ate her—"an eye for an eye, a tooth for a tooth" but not the head. This we left for the butcher, to sell to whomever likes what we don't. I didn't feel towards her the way I did when we ate Norman the young steer, for she was bad and deserved to die, besides, we were out of pork in the locker, and had none ready to put in.

Strange as it may seem to many, the pig is the cleanest animal on the farm, quick to learn if given half a chance. Each farrowing pen is scrubbed and disinfected between litters. Here, as in the large pen where the sow spent her waiting period, she is quick to learn that the dry section where all the straw is piled will stay that way if she makes her manure in one spot where it is a little wet. Even the little pigs learn this before they are weaned. When dewormed, they are taken to their new quarters to find a large dry section to sleep in and a damp one for sanitary purposes. They keep it this way. So, all the manure is made in the cleaning alley where, when the doors are closed to separate it from the dry pen, it is easily cleaned, saving time and straw.

In talking to Alfred about his grassland programme, the question often comes up, "What will you do for straw?"

"To date, I have not had to worry about that. There are still many farmers unaware of its true value, ready and anxious to sell it. With my harvester I can pick up combined straw in the fields, and if it is not a long haul it is a very practical thing for me to do. So I buy straw and fill my barn to capacity."

Of course, there is always the odd pig who wants to be contrary or is not quite as intelligent as the others, and will have dirty habits. These are cured in short order by leaving no straw whatsoever in the area where manure is to be made. The pig soon finds it more comfortable if the straw is kept scrupulously dry, a little more work for the attendant for a day or so, but well worth the effort in time saved later, if nothing else. No pig wants to sleep where it is wet and dirty, nor will it be as thrifty if it has to.

These pigs are hardy, making vigorous growth, arriving at market weight in from four and one-half to five months of age. Alfred will not sell any under twelve weeks of age for breeding stock, at which time their conformation will have shown up. Feeding has been from the beginning an interesting factor in the enterprise, having an important influence on the health and profitable aspects of the business.

With the litter of nine weanlings, Alfred had had remarkable success in feeding grass silage, and in the spectacular improvement in health of the paralyzed pig, as well as cutting feeding costs in half and producing Grade "A" Select pigs in record time. He pays very special attention to his feeding practices, which are carried right through from feeding the sow before she farrows, to starting the young pigs on into market weight or saleable age for breeding stock.

The young pigs are started in their creep on the best known brand of starter checkers to supplement what they obtain nursing. After weaning, gradually over a four-week period this is changed till they are getting one part hog concentrate mixed with five parts western oats in the form of dry chop. There are water bowls in each pen to which the pigs have free access at all times. This feeding is continued till the pig is ready for market. All the pigs get silage when the pit is opened, every morning. Even the little pigs at two weeks old show a marked liking for it and give the mother close competition for a share. The day a sow farrows, she rarely wants to eat, showing no inclination for her chop, but will always eat silage and with relish. There is something in it she requires and for this reason will eat. Animals are more discerning or conscious of their body requirements than humans who favour what tickles their palates. A pig seeks that which it requires for health, and we have found silage of good quality necessary in our regular feeding programme.

The red tape involved in registering, transferring ownership, naming and numbering this superior specimen of the pork family involves a lot of time. It means keeping up statistics, as well as selecting the best from every litter for breeding purposes. We consider it well worth while in our effort to improve the breed, making it more profitable for the farmer of today and the future. Nothing but the best is worthy of our name "Eloradale, bred on Friendship Farm."

CHAPTER 18

When I, halfheartedly, remonstrated with Alfred for spending so much money on the house, bringing in all the conveniences we wanted in one fell swoop, he remarked, "You helped me from the beginning. It would not be fair to have everything up-to-date and perfect on the farm, while you struggled along with antiquated makeshifts."

"I know, but in the house, it doesn't bring returns."

"It brings self-respect and dignity. The enterprise cannot run well if it is off-balance or lop-sided. We will bring everything up to a high standard together."

So I feel pampered. It's delightful. I revel in it. Turning a tap, hot water! Cold! A flick of my finger and the heat, or air conditioning comes on. Another flick and it is off. No more hot fires in summer to heat the sad irons when there is a large ironing to do, or baking. I can make a cake whenever I wish; just turn the oven on and it is ready when the batter is. Looking out over the spotless white porcelain sink to the crab-apple tree, I see my large flat stone where lawn chairs next year will be placed conveniently near. Here I will do my mending and reading, have mid-morning coffee with Alfred and talk of the day's occupations. A gentle sloping lawn, green and lush, landscaped the summer before, with flowers everywhere! The twenty-one varieties of iris Bob gave us, border a flagstone walk, with the same number of best known varieties of gladioli in the kitchen garden beyond. I had heard a friend once talk of having their garden landscaped, but never dreamed that I would have this done here on the farm. Once, to a V.L.A. official the desire had been expressed and quickly noted. They brought their landscape expert and mapped out the garden for Alfred and me.

So, I look beyond the garden to the cattle, cows now with calves close by, and larger ones, aloof, independent, but liking companionship, always near. It is close to sunset, and the long rays of the sun turn the tree trunk to golden brown and bring out the vivid green of the long grasses and legumes the cattle stand in, with it touching their bellies. I wonder if the animals know they are beautiful in this light at this hour, with the sun bringing out the red brown sheen of their coats and their white markings in strong relief, with every colour and tone intense, clearcut, to be well remembered when dusk falls with promise for another beautiful day. The cattle have chosen the best possible moment to show off their beauty as they parade across my vision, creatures of habit seeking a tender special morsel for their evening grazing, while wending their leisurely way round to the spring for water. "The parade of the stars" we call it, and to us it is just that, and gratifying indeed to look upon.

We commenced our farm life with the urgent need of a steady weekly income, cows producing milk, to be sold as whole milk or separated for cream, collected at the door daily or weekly according to the form the product was sold in. For this we were paid each week, and to the farmer who does not consider his time of any value, or the crop he grows on his fields, it is money in hand, profits.

Unfortunately, we found that the method of marketing the milk lowered our profitable enterprise to an unprofitable one. Neither manufacturers' milk nor cream paid enough to merit all the expense in feeding, or the amount of work involved. With a milk contract unobtainable, pig and poultry production increased and left more net profit, so we changed to beef cattle. Unable at the time to buy beef cows for breeding purposes, we could invest in stock calves, buying them at between three and four hundred pounds, for a long keep.

The year we were still in dairy work, the production on our land was so poor that we had to sell seven nice heifers for lack of feed. In the first three years we could not feed more than fourteen cows. The fourth year we carried twenty-three beef cattle; the fifth year, thirty-two. The sixth year we had forty-eight, and this year, seventy. This spectacular rise in our carrying ability was due entirely to the study and treatment of the soil. Alfred will not be satisfied until he is maintaining ninety head of cattle on ninety acres of land, winter and summer.

The ten good beef Hereford grade cows, along with eight young heifers from a similar Hereford grade lot of stock calves bred the previous year, are the basis of our beef breeding herd. In the early fall when the eight heifers were about ready to be bred, Alfred and I set out to find a good pure bred bull, as it is a well-known fact a good bull is fifty per cent of a herd, a bad one is ninety, and we want to raise good quality beef.

We started out with a lead. This one took us below Rockwood. We saw the bull and Alfred liked his qualities; but he is never rushed when he is buying. We went in to a farm and walked down a lane, through a corn field, along a willow bank, to see a bull to be put up for sale at the farm auction the following day. He eyed us casually as we respectfully looked him over.

"Too rough."

On then to Hillsburgh. On the way we bought our winter's supply of potatoes from a farmer in the field. After supper we went north to Teviotdale; again the bull wasn't quite good enough. It was a lovely day; we were together all of it, and had so much to talk about. The next day we were back below Rockwood to buy the first bull Alfred had looked at. When he took over his harem and looked so regal amongst them, we were well pleased, having looked at sixteen bulls before deciding on him. He'll give us good calves, we feel sure. We disregarded his pedigree name and gave him one of our own choosing. It will be the name he is known by here. It is Matt, after my father and my brother whom we duly notified of the honour.

"Man, he's a beauty," Dad said as he walked round and round admiring all our stock, which up till now had never quite met with his approval. I think he used to make excuses for us, but now he likes to come to the farm and walk through the barn or fields gloating over the beautiful animals.

"Man. You should show them, Alfred," he would say. "You'd get all firsts."

I well remembered the day when Dad, and an uncle interested only in beef cattle, had disparaged our dairy herd with casual remarks about the poor showing they made in comparison with the sleek, fat beef cattle we should own. Those cattle were our best possible effort at that time. I sizzled. No man could belittle my husband, not even my father, and how close they came that day to being ordered off the place they never knew.

It was all different now, and we liked to see Dad enjoying his hours on the farm, looking at the pigs and cattle and the busy productive chickens.

In the loafing barn, the cattle move about freely, quiet when we walk amongst them, nuzzling for a little attention and head scratching. The winter had come early and in November they spent most of their time in the shelter of the barn, although free to come and go through the barnyard down the lane to the spring on the edge of the cedar grove. I often watched them from the kitchen window as they came and went at will. Many of the ten bred heifers were due to freshen soon. Not having a record of breeding, we could only guess, so Alfred kept close watch over them.

It was St. Andrew's day. A pig was due to farrow and we had gone to the barn to see her, as usual looking over the entire stock, pigs and cattle, during our leisurely visit. The snow had left, but came again that night. There was a lovely carpet of white over all the fields, and a moon almost full, to intensify the beauty of the night. Alfred walked through the loafing barn, looking at each heifer, then again counting all the cattle. He counted them in the barnyard and stood at the head of the lane to count any he might see on their way to or from the spring.

"There is one missing. It may be beyond the bend. It's the heifer with the pure white face and no white markings on her body. She is due to freshen soon. I'll have to find her if she isn't there in an hour."

She wasn't there; so putting on warmer clothing and getting a flashlight to use in the cedars, Alfred set out to find the heifer. Methodically he followed the fence down to the line fence by the bush, to the back of the farm, then up on the cleared spot above the cedars. Here he stopped to listen. A twig snapped, and another. A low moo, warning of a mother to her child to lie low. Following the sound, Alfred found them. Nestled in a sheltered spot amongst the cedars lay a new-born calf, still wet and standing by its mother. Talking gently to it, Alfred lifted the calf to his shoulders and, holding its legs around his neck, prepared to tramp home through the snow. As he did so, he was startled to find the heifer Margaret close beside, and from the footprints in the snow he could see she had been with him all the time as he searched the fence corners, following so quietly that he didn't even hear her footfall. So the man with his burden followed by an anxious mother, trudged through the new fallen snow back to the barn, where mother and calf were made snug and warm in a special section reserved for them. He was a nice bull calf, born on St. Andrew's day, so we called him Andrew.

During the summer, when there are new calves born in the meadow, Alfred watches them closely for a day or so to be sure all is well with mother and calf. One afternoon, towards the end of the day, he remarked to me he had not seen a new calf all day. The cattle were all in the field they always chose at this hour, to give us our "Parade of the Stars," so Alfred, Jim and I went out to see if we could find it. The mother was easy to spot, for she was apprehensive and not grazing, watching us closely. Seeing that she had been sucked recently, her udder being soft, we were not afraid anything had happened to the calf, unless, of course, one of the milk thieves amongst the older calves had been at her. Each of us, taking a strip, keeping the same distance apart and with an eye on the wary mother, we proceeded to search slowly through the long lush grasses, over the hill. Away from the grazing cattle, on down the slope we went, and turning, saw the mother's head appear over the rise. She was watching us. We went the length of the field and were coming back, when a warning call from the mother told us one of us was close; but no calf could be seen. Suddenly, Jim called,

"Here it is."

Sure enough, all curled up and half asleep, looking wonderingly at us, lay a beautiful calf. Its mother was almost immediately at its side.

Content that all was well, we returned to the house. We are never able to take for granted this wonderful instinct of mother love in our animal life.

There had been a like experience in the same field when Alfred and Otto searched for a baby calf and, giving up, returned to the house. Turning for a last look back over the field, they saw the little vixen standing in the long grass looking at them. When Alfred turned towards it, it lay down again. I'm definitely certain they play tag when half a dozen get together and, kicking their heels high in the air, dash up and down slopes, one after the other, and pause to bunt before they are off again on another wild chase.

In this little world on which we live, the cycle of life goes on under the guidance of Nature and pure animal instinct, keeping it all in economical balance to suit our design. This hundred acres of land is ours to rule over. How wonderful it would be if the whole world could be kept in such perfect balance that neither man nor beast would starve, and life would have the dignity and natural beauty that are its heritage. With civilization, I wonder, have we lost the simplicity of perfect beauty? Are we really the superior beings we think we are just because we control, or think we do, the destiny of the animal kingdom?

It's a pleasure to go down to the barn now in the winter when all the stock is in, to watch the animals moving quietly about or lying in a favourite spot in the loafing area. No rush or bustle for feed. No necessity to push one another out of the way, because they know all they have to do is to get up and walk over to the feeding manger where hay is contained, and which is never allowed to be empty. This manger lies directly below the hay mow along one wall, and was designed by Alfred so that hay could be taken direct from the mow and dropped down. As it piles up in the manger it is pushed first one way then the other till the racks are full, using a minimum of labour. It was also designed to act as a cattle chute with a door, and when it is open cattle driven round by the opposite entrance, shut off from escape, are forced to enter. It is about thirty feet in length, so designed that they can't turn around. At the far end of the chute is a stanchion door where each animal in turn is fastened by the neck and easily handled for whatever treatment it was put in there for— T.B. testing, inoculations, dehorning or delousing. As each one is released, the doors swing outward and they are driven directly into the barnyard till all are treated, and there is no possible chance of their getting mixed up. This is a definite must in a loafing barn. Before we had this, each animal had to be lassoed and snubbed to a post. This can become quite a task.

If the cattle are not in a mood for dry hay, they can walk over to the conveyor manger which runs forty-five feet along an opposite wall coming directly out of the trench silo. Here there is grass silage at all times. This conveyor was designed jointly by the McKee Brothers and Alfred to suit our specifications. The conveyor is two feet wide, one foot deep, set up three feet off the floor, being slightly lower at one end for the young fry, with a heavy manger built in front so the cattle can't damage the conveyor. As the silage is emptied from the silo directly on to the conveyor, merely by adding another eight foot length and letting out a little more cable it saves the necessity of ever having to throw the silage any more than eight feet at the maximum. As the face of the silage is moved back down the full length of the eighty foot silo, so the conveyor follows closely, by adding another eight foot length, leaving it necessary to handle the silage, like the hay, just once. With the water working on a float in the water trough, and salt and mineral always available, our cattle lounge in luxurious comfort and plenty, undisturbed by people working around them.

Getting a high protein feed in the silage and good hay, and having a herd of nurse cows, calves and growing stock, these animals never get expensive mill feeds. Forage is a natural feed for foraging animals and Alfred is convinced that you can't make money feeding cattle with a scoop shovel and grain feeding. For growth and health, you can't beat good grass silage and good hay as feed, nor can you finish cattle as easily, quickly, or as cheaply as on a good improved pasture mixture. We know because we've done it. We have had cattle that have been here for a year and six months, coming in as calves and going out as choice weighty steers, leaving behind a very tidy profit. They are fed in winter on the cheapest and easiest forage a farmer can grow, and in the summer with their own standard equipment, a four-inch cutter bar, on, not a little timothy and June grass, but lush legumes and grasses. All this brings to mind a story that Alfred told me.

He was standing in the butcher shop one day talking to his friend the butcher; it was mid-morning, and he was there for nearly half an hour. There were two sides of pork hanging on the meat rack on which the skin was becoming transparent, the meat having hung there for several weeks. There were cuts of beef in the cooling cabinet starting to turn dark. A woman walked in.

"Give me four slices of cooked ham, please." Served, she walked out. After an interval, another woman walked in.

"I'll take a pound of summer sausage." Two customers in half an hour. With the butcher business desperate it made Alfred feel depressed. There was only one answer to all this. Beef was thirty-nine cents a pound on the hoof, live weight. Mrs. Consumer couldn't afford to buy meat, and nobody was happy, the producer, the wholesaler, retailer or consumer. It took a catastrophe in the form of foot and mouth disease to right this wrong.

Alfred had occasion again to visit his friend in the butcher shop at the same time of day. On the meat racks that ran the side of the shop hung beef and pork carcasses. Three butchers were working at top speed, and still they couldn't keep customers from waiting to be served. One woman asked for "Four sirloin steaks, please. I'll take a couple of those broilers and some bacon."

The butcher wrapped about one and a half pounds of sliced bacon and she was off. Another said:

"I'd like a short rib roast and a couple of pounds of hamburger, some sausage, about a couple of pounds. Oh yes, some bacon."

Another pound and a half of bacon was wrapped up. She was gone and Alfred just stood there and glowed. People could afford to eat meat again. He knew that by the method of feeding he had arrived at between the two periods of high and moderate priced meat, he could still produce beef at twenty-five cents a pound and make as much profit as the grain feeding farmers were making at thirty-nine. The sight of those people able to purchase meat again made us feel good.

CHAPTER 19

Society is a partnership in all science; a partnership in
all art; a partnership in every virtue and in all perfec-
tion. As the ends of such a partnership cannot be
obtained in many generations, it becomes a partnership
not only between those who are living but between
those who are living, those who are dead and those who
are to be born.

—Edmund Burke.

I have related the story of the spectacular improvement in fertility and production on our farm and the exciting developments that resulted. We sought the cause of our inability to
produce enough on our farm to provide the standard of living
we wished to attain, and putting personal comfort aside dealt
with the problem that would give us what we desired. We knew
after two years cropping in the habitual manner of the district
that we were fighting a losing battle against nature. We had put
all we possessed into this farm, we loved the solitude and freedom of the country, and were determined to stay. Proud, we
would not grovel for the crumbs this farm could produce, nor
were we content to adjust the standard of living we had been
accustomed to in order to exist here.

Alfred had been a good soldier. He was a good one still. He
studied, and used the Ontario Agricultural College, as it is
intended to be used, for the improvement of agriculture. He
was fortunate to live nearby and be able to visit the college
whenever he desired to talk and discuss agriculture with men
who had specialized in the fields he was interested in. In many
instances we were breaking away from known and proven
methods practised at the college. We had to, with no financial
backing to support a long-term improvement that on our farm
would probably take our life time. We were in a very different

position from the average farmer whose land is in good tilth which he is able to maintain, and which, if he is content with the financial returns its production brings he is rarely interested in improving.

It is a well-known fact that land once in good tilth will, if wrongly used, eventually return to nature, the great healer. This farm was in the process of being taken back by nature. We merely interrupted her relentless progress for a short time with our methods of plowing, cultivating, and seeding to shallow rooted grain crops. We could not fight her progress, but we could work with her.

There is great beauty in the mantle nature spreads over the tortured earth while under it the processes of life are renewed. This farm, when we bought it, was green with twitch grass, working with its tremendous root system to renew the organic matter so depleted as to be non-existent. Bladder campion, devil's paintbrush, thistles, golden rod flourished. On one low flat where a brush lot had been, now knolls and gullies where the trees had been uprooted, mullein thrived like a child imitating his soldierly father, standing straight and growing tall, but not able to take the place of the trees that once stood there. Mullein grows where the land is poor, and this was poor indeed, pathetic in its beautiful poverty, when devil's paintbrush was in bloom and mullein a misty green. Winding cowpaths and rocks lay across its surface, a long low stretch of tortured land, useless to man and beast. Between the cedar grove and swamp of a neighbouring farm, a muddy creek told its story of erosion, as it wound its way around and through beautiful undergrowth, tall elms and hemlock, willows and wild raspberry bushes, to the river, running muddy torrents in the spring.

There were originally fifteen inches of top soil on the earth. Now there are only seven to produce the world's food supply. There are millions of microorganisms and bacteria in a thimbleful of top soil; more life in that little bit of earth than in the population of New York City, providing that it is good rich earth. It is from this top soil that we get our food supply. Therefore, the biggest loss on the farm is from erosion. Here we must start to preserve what we still have.

As you drive along the highway in winter, wherever a bare field is passed the snow on the roadside is brown. Three times one winter after a wind storm Alfred noted this, and it was still January with months of wind storms yet to come before the ground would be covered with a protective growth. A tremendous amount of top soil, mineral and humus must be lost in this way. On our land, with nothing but light sand or gravel on the knolls and black earth on our flats, the story of erosion was evident.

"It is the last year that I will have fields left bare in winter or any other time," Alfred vowed.

One year later at a Soil and Crop Improvement Convention in Toronto, Alfred learned from a lecture given by Dr. Harrold of Cochocton, Ohio, that in a normal year on a five per cent slope bare ground will lose, through wind and water erosion, twenty-two pounds of nitrogen per acre, plus a comparable percentage of other basic minerals.

There is no economy in leaving fields bare and losing over winter what must be replaced at a terrific expense every spring by commercial fertilizers. Soil losses from erosion can be cut to zero by keeping the ground covered in winter; therefore, the farmer using commercial fertilizer in the spring will be building up his fertility at no added cost, instead of just replacing his losses year after year as so many do to the detriment of their economy and land fertility. It is also well known that trash or stubble on a field will slow the wind velocity by eight miles an hour.

The equivalent of a two-inch rainfall will be absorbed in ten minutes on a high organic open soil. On hard packed soil, low in organic matter, it will take over an hour. If there is any slope, most of it will run off. Bacteria need moisture. Fertility depends on bacteria. Bacteria depend on organic matter.

We had to stop erosion and increase our organic matter. The fertility would follow. The micro-organisms in the soil had to be maintained and increased before the soil could give us any appreciable increase in production, maintain and improve it.

Alfred searched for the method of tillage that would suit his land best. It varied from sand to loam to clay in different fields. Knowing the benefits of open soil and organic matter, he sees no reason why his methods cannot be applied with benefit to a very large percentage of the land in Ontario. There are many farms in Ontario and Canada that are in good tilth and on which good farmers are maintaining the degree of tilth and fertility they have without improving it.

Cover crops were the answer to the problem of stopping erosion.

(1) Fall wheat is a natural cover crop and can assist greatly in stepping up a changeover by also supplying a cash crop when that factor is important to the individual farmer's needs. After the wheat is harvested, one-way disc the straw into the soil and sow immediately oats. These will give excellent fall pasture, as in their green state they contain twenty-six per cent protein, and will act as a cover crop over winter.

(2) Fall rye. This we used as our first cover crop, but rejected it in favour of oats because the rye is a biennial and comes up the following year in the seeded crop.

(3) Sweet clover, particularly where grain is to be sown two years running. The first year it will give fall pasture and cover over winter with the added benefit of two and a half tons of root system to the acre, more than any other cover crop, thus increasing the organic matter appreciably. It also helps inoculate the soil for the oncoming legumes. It is a biennial and will come up in the seeded crop the following year.

(4) Green oats we prefer because they do not bother us in the following crop, the oats being dead in the spring.

According to reports from outside sources, we are operating our farm with a minimum of equipment. This consists of (1) One power unit, a tractor strong enough to handle all operations without working to capacity; (2) A one-man forage harvester and wagon; (3) A deep tillage cultivator; (4) One-way disc; (5) Set of diamond harrows; (6) A seeder; (7) A manure spreader—a mowing machine with windrow attachment. The tractor is equipped with hydraulic control live-power take-off, belt pulley and front-end loader.

A field of sod that is going to be broken up first of all has a crop of grass silage or pasture taken off. About the middle of June, it is gone over once or twice with the deep tillage cultivator to a depth of about twelve inches. It is one-way disced once to a depth of six to seven inches. These operations are done at the speed of from two-and-a-half to three miles an hour because a faster speed tends to too much smashing of the soil and a breaking down of the soil structure which it is so important to keep. Soil structure is one of the most important features of good soil, and if man destroys this structure, he defeats his own purpose.

It is only necessary to dig into an old fence row to see what lovely, crumb-like soil nature has built there through the years. In fields that were like blowsand, the worm population was nil. Now in the same fields with good soil structure and high organic content, the worm population increased tremendously. Under grass, the feeder roots always growing and decaying, along with the bacteria action and worm population, help to make this excellent crumb-like soil structure. To preserve the soil structure, field operations should be kept to an absolute minimum, and then only at speeds that will not crush and destroy it, with tillage equipment that will aerate and mix the trash.

Thus, we have used the deep tillage cultivator once or twice and the one-way disc once. Now we sow five pecks of buckwheat to the acre. This is allowed to grow to a height of from two to three feet, then one-way disced to mix this green manure in the soil. The discing is followed immediately by the sowing of three bushels of oats to the acre. This in three or four weeks time, depending on the growing season, will usually give two-and-a-half months of good fall pasture of a very high protein forage.

When the snow has come and gone, as it will do many times perhaps throughout the winter, this field is a picture, with its lush green carpet showing through the pure white snow. The oats stooled out through grazing cover the field with a thick mat; not a row of the seeding shows. By this method two crops have been harvested and one crop of green manure returned to the soil in the one crop year, with a minimum of operations and time involved. The following spring this ground is manured; the manure taken directly from the loafing barn to be spread on the field, followed closely by the one-way disc and the deep tillage cultivator adjusted to shallow cultivation with the diamond harrows attached behind. Each operation is done only once. It is then seeded immediately to a mixture of grasses and legumes, with a nurse crop of five pecks of oats to the acre. The oats will be either combined or pastured and clipped.

Visualize here the amount of organic matter that has gone back into the soil with: (1) Old sod; (2) Buckwheat; (3) Root system of the cover crop; (4) Manure.

A grass silage crop and two-and-a-half months of excellent pasture were also harvested. During the fall when the meadows are at rest, Alfred, Jim and I will have walked over the entire farm, gathering our soil samples which we place in the convenient little brown boxes supplied by the Soils Department of our Ontario Agricultural College. Carefully labelled, they are mailed or delivered in person to the Department. On the return of the soils analysis, Alfred will sow on the field, whose tillage was just described, with the grass and legume mixture and nurse crop of oats, the recommended fertilizer from his soils analysis. It is very interesting to watch the improvement each year in these reports, and compare them with the physical improvement we can see in the growth and production on the field.

Our reason for using a deep tillage cultivator and one-way disc is this: In putting so much sod, buckwheat and manure into the soil, had it been plowed under rather than mixed in with the deep tillage cultivator and one-way disc, the trash would have been mummified for too long a period, forming a blotter cutting off the capillary system of the subsoil and would be too intense for the bacteria to work easily. A fine silt of subsoil, the result of plowing deep, should be kept away from the surface where it will tend to seal off absorption. Bacteria require a lot of moisture which they have to get from the rainfall and through the capillary system developed in good soil structure. Plowing thus increases erosion, as it leaves the surface almost entirely void of organic matter, and unguarded against wind erosion and the splash of the raindrop that shatters the soil and seals it off. This gives you water erosion, with eighty-five per cent to ninety per cent of a heavy shower leaving the place where it fell to end up in the creek bed with much of your rich top soil, your difference between profit and loss.

On a piece of land that has been reseeded, this leaves the seeds and small plants wanting moisture. Where a trash mulch is in and on top of the soil you have eighty-five per cent to

ninety per cent saturation. This will supply the necessary moisture for germination and growth over a period of several weeks.
It is in the quick spring showers that we have to capture as
much moisture as possible. By using the method of mixing in,
a portion of the refuse or trash is left on the surface of the soil,
which prevents shattering of the soil by heavy raindrops. All
operations are followed closely by seeding something as it is
natural for soil to have growth on it. It is unnatural for a field to
be bare, either by open summer fallow, which we found a waste
of growing time, and as our experiments have proved is not as
good as growing a green crop and working it in, or by fall plowing and leaving it bare over the long winter months.

By keeping something growing on the fields, we are aiding
nature in the cycle of birth, growth, death and decay. A cover
crop is absolutely necessary to the improvement of the practice
of agriculture. It also acts as a catch crop, inasmuch as the crop
residue worked into the soil makes it immediately available to
the bacteria that attack it at once. Here, trash farming enlists
the aid of those millions of bacteria now working for us.

During the first few years, with our limited number of livestock, we couldn't begin to cover any appreciable percentage of
the farm with barnyard manure. Our organic matter and fertility had to come from another source. Chemical fertilizer and
trash proved to be a very good answer to the problem. Straw
disced in after the combine was the first trash used, then green
manures.

This year, between a compost heap treated with bacteria
and our year's manure, we will have enough to cover the entire
farm.

By getting as much trash as possible into the soil, the soil
is not only aerated but given a spongelike structure that
absorbs rainfall. In our case, where there had been hard clay
with no topsoil over it, the addition of great quantities of trash
and organic matter softened the clay to a crumb-like soil structure. The knolls began to turn dark once more and stay green
through dry spells in the hot summer months. A field may look
trashy after fitting and seeding, but we certainly get a wonderful germination and catch of grasses and legumes.

Because of the very open, porous, crumbly mulch that
seems to resist heaving we have yet to have our clovers and

alfalfas heaved out of the ground by frost. It is hard to freeze and expand a substance that isn't solid and hard packed. We know bacteria provide warmth if present in sufficient numbers. Could it also be, then, that the tremendous increase in bacteria in our soil is preventing frost from getting to any appreciable depth? The bacteria cycle depends entirely on the presence of organic matter, humus and air in the soil. It is an important study in itself; this is a simple outline of how it functions in the soil. Multiplication is rapid; three generations a day.

Two types of bacteria are in the soil: aerobic and anaerobic. The aerobic bacteria, depending in numbers on the amount of surface and aeration in the soil, extract the free nitrogen from the air and keep it near the surface. The anaerobic bacteria which, in turn, devour the aerobic bacteria, deposit the nitrogen to a greater depth in the soil. In hard packed, poorly aerated soil, low in organic matter, there is a limited amount of plant food, and plants will grow on it, but plant roots cannot break down and feed on the minute particles of soil, so evidence of various deficiencies in the plant will appear. Where there is an abundance of organic matter, humus and aeration, the bacteria count in the soil is increased a thousandfold. The mineral content of the trash devoured by the bacteria is obtainable in their secretions by plant roots. Bacteria also assist in the breaking down of these minute particles of soil which contain mineral, therefore the more bacteria, the more breakdown of the soil into immediately available plant food.

If there is no plant growing on the surface, as in the case of open summer fallow and fall plowing, then all these millions of allied workers are working for nothing. That is why our cover crop and fall pasture also serves as a catch crop, inasmuch as the stubble or trash that has been mixed in with the soil is being decomposed and devoured by the bacteria. (This process commences almost immediately). These mineral secretions from the bacteria are available, and if there is not a crop growing on top with roots reaching down into the soil to extract the mineral and plant nutrients as it is secreted, then nature automatically locks it in the soil and it becomes unavailable for later use.

This cover crop also serves another excellent purpose. In the fall from the middle of September to the middle of October when the legumes, particularly the alfalfa, are storing up energy for the winter, the less grazing on it the better. With the young oats high in protein at this time, you don't have any extra work in closing the cattle off from the alfalfa. Just let them have access to the green oats and they will confine their grazing mostly to them.

The first year the McK.ee Brothers were out helping Alfred adjust the new harvester in a very heavy field of clover they were having trouble adjusting the pickup. It was either too high or too low.

"No wonder we can't get it just right," one of the brothers remarked. "The rubber tires of the harvester are sinking an inch deep in the earth. It is so springy."

Bluntly Alfred replied,

"What are you complaining about? Don't you realize it has taken me five years to get the soil in that condition. How else do you think I got such a good crop on this field?"

"I don't know, but it's twice as good as anything we've grown when we were farming."

"I have to have a harvester that will handle a good crop."

"You will have one."

We have. The brothers were as good as their word. We don't have to worry about weeds any more, for they thrive only on poor land. On a high fertility soil we have found they can't compete, not even twitch grass, with orchard and brome grass. By clipping the pastures, noxious weeds are discouraged and not allowed to reseed themselves.

The farmer who sows one bag of fertilizer to the acre is serving one purpose only, and it is an unprofitable one, on land that has been exposed to the detrimental effects of being left bare over the winter. One bag of fertilizer to the acre will produce a larger root system on grain than no fertilizer will, but it doesn't apply enough mineral to complete the job it starts, thereby leaving the land much poorer and lower in fertility than it already was. The extra root system developed by the application of the fertilizer is going to take more from the soil than it could normally give had no fertilizer been used and a normal root had grown in proportion to the mineral fertility of the soil at that time. Therefore, the idea that a little fertilizer is better than none is false. It is equally impractical to choose by guesswork a chemical fertilizer, and the amount required one thinks sufficient, without the soils analysis report to go by. Farming is a long term project. We can't take everything this year and leave nothing for next. Sowing one bag of fertilizer hastens the deterioration of the soil. The key to the yield is soil structure, and a healthy soil is not infested with insects.

Everything cannot be accomplished at once. In our case, the use of sweet clover as a cover crop hastened our programme of cover crops over the entire farm when we were in a state of transition, changing over from growing cereal grains to grass and legume mixtures. We were determined to grow what was best for our soil. Row crops were absolutely out, from the standpoint of erosion as well as being the most expensive to produce. Corn, a row crop, was also hard on the soil from a structural point of view. Economically, it was unsound for us. The cost of purchasing expensive equipment necessary for handling, and the time lost working in large groups to harvest it, eliminated corn for us from the beginning. Alfred could grow as much grass and legume forage per acre as he could corn, and get more protein as well.

In studying the economic advantages of a grassland farm programme, Alfred came up with some very interesting facts in his reading which led to the startling discovery that he could not afford to grow cereal grain from a nutrient value point of view alone.

A crop of grain averaging eighty bushels to the acre would produce three hundred pounds of available nutrients to the acre, at a cost of eighteen dollars and fifty cents per acre, which includes fitting, seeding and harvesting. By growing a mixture of grasses and legumes he could produce upward of fifteen hundred pounds of available nutrients at a cost of nine dollars and fifty cents per acre which, includes fitting, seeding and harvesting, the same amount of chemical fertilizer used for the grass as for the grain. These figures do not include fixed costs. As to the effect on soil, it is common knowledge that grass is the great healer, and sod is the best possible means of building soil structure and permanent fertility. The fertility of the soil can be built up better under grass and legume sod than under any other conditions. Grain, being a shallow rooted crop gives little or nothing to the soil; and if the soil happened to be low in fertility, the grain too would be low in nutritional and mineral value. Choosing the deep rooted grasses and legumes, rather than the shallow rooted grain crops, you extract the untapped wealth of mineral in the subsoil.

On our land, depending on the proportion of grasses and legumes, the fields are only broken up and reseeded every five to eight years, according to the proportions of carbohydrate and protein required for a well balanced forage. Alfred tries to have sixty per cent legume and forty per cent grass. When this reverts to forty per cent legume and sixty per cent grass, then it is broken up and reseeded in the method described. This does away with a terrific amount of fall and spring work. All the field work is done in summer and seldom more than fifteen acres at a time. Grain farmers usually seed, on a hundred acre farm, about forty or fifty acres every spring, which requires a rush season that in turn requires fall plowing.

With grassland farming able to grow more nutrients to the acre than grain farming at less cost and labour involved, Alfred solved for himself the problem he commenced farming with—a physical disability making long, hard labour impossible to continue.

We have felt it a great pity that the average farmer feels a hundred acre farm cannot support more than one family. His son must seek work either as hired farm help which in too many cases is seasonal, or go to the city. We are able to keep permanent hired help and at the same time support a standard of living to our taste, with the secure knowledge that our economic practices are sound. Disciple of no man, Alfred keeps an open mind. If a practice, now good, becomes unsound and injurious to the soil, he will find a better way and follow it.

During the summer of 1953, Dr. Richards, head of the Soils Department, O.A.C. (who can't visit this farm too often, for every minute he spends here gives Alfred a chance to ask more questions and receive more valuable information from this advanced scientist) spent a whole afternoon here with the college photographer, taking pictures of the different crops, check plots, and land use methods. This was for the purpose of supplying a group of Junior Farmers, who were to visit here later, with a set of slides for each Junior Farmers' Club in Ontario. Having seen the actual fields, and heard Alfred speak on their development and answer innumerable questions, they could pass on what they had seen and heard to their clubs during the winter. They walked round the farm together, each one asking and answering questions on Alfred's favourite topic, "soils." Coming to rest on the high hill that centred the farm, and looking over the lush crops and abundant growth, Dr. Richards asked, "What crop rotation do you carry out?"

Alfred replied, "None."

Contemplating this statement and its significance, Dr. Richards remarked, "You have great faith in your soil."

Alfred quietly replied, "Yes."

Having developed an economically sound agriculture on run-out land, we have visitors, interested in improved practices from all over Ontario, many making return trips. It is wonderful to have this first-hand proof that the Canadian farmer is not content with his present economic state, is concerned about fertility problems and is looking for new ideas to put into practice. We have had letters from every part of Canada, and groups from England and U.S.A., every one alert, interested and stimulating to talk with.

The quiet life we sought is still ours, and we have a great sense of well being and the feeling that we are being useful and justifying our existence. The sanctity of our home is protected by a spiritual strength gained in working in harmony with nature, content in the possession of each day.

"It is good," we tell one another.

Late in the fall of 1952, Alfred had a visitor who had come up from the College, where he had heard of Alfred's work, to ask him if he would speak in January at the annual meeting of the Industrial and Development Council of Canadian Meat Packers on "A Farmer's Approach to Livestock Production Costs."

By now, nothing could surprise us, unless it should be a long period with no letters or visitors, and that situation had not yet developed. People were still coming, still interested in the soil and what it could produce if handled with understanding. Alfred, liking our visitor, could not refuse, and we forgot about it temporarily, since the meeting was still a long time away. Then, one day, a letter came,

"Will you please send us a copy of your talk to be mimeo-graphed."

This was different. Accustomed, now, to impromptu dis-cussions and answering questions, giving a written paper was quite another thing.

"I don't think I'll do it."

"Of course you will. It's at Niagara Falls. We haven't been there in winter and I want to go. I've missed every speaking engagement you have had and this I don't intend missing."

My chin was out.

So, Alfred wrote his talk, and this was to outshine his pre-vious "shining hour." It outlines more economical methods of producing livestock and poultry products, a subject of great interest to the consuming public and of importance to the eco-nomic future of our agriculture. Alfred was the last speaker on the last day of the convention, yet he held his audience with these remarks, speaking as he was for the first time to a national group.

The Junior Farmer Group from England, as well as a pre-vious visit from one of their Agricultural Representatives, brought to Alfred's mind months he had spent working on English farms during his army service. They had much to talk about.

Sponsored by the Economics Department at O.A.C., a group of clergymen taking a summer course in agriculture vis-ited us one hot August afternoon. We were expecting them, so I had ice cold drinks ready. Thirteen spiritual advisors from possibly as many religious denominations sat together in our living room in friendly conversation with one another, accept-ing our hospitality, all interested in one thing, agriculture, and its relation to God and man. Questions and answers flew back and forth, faces shone with enthusiasm, as the tremendous sig-nificance of working with nature was discussed from a practical individual's standpoint. There were clerics from Sweden, Czechoslovakia, and Israel, and all over Ontario, amongst them; some with a very definite foreign accent. When they were gone, we watched the last one go down the drive and clasping hands, remarked quietly in unison, "Is good, is good."

Dr. Richards and Ontario Government Agricultural offi-cials returned with their group of Junior Farmer Representatives to tour the farm. Standing on the high hill, "the top of the world," Dr. Richards spoke to his class:

"You have seen contour work and its benefits, here you see conservation practised to the utmost," he said.

Later, our own Wellington County Agricultural Representative accompanied a twilight tour of six county farms, each important for some special feature developed into a sound economical practice. Standing with Alfred beside the trench silo addressing a hundred and fifty farmers and their families, Mr. Black, introducing Alfred said:

"Seven years ago, when Alf bought this farm it was run out, one of the poorest in the county. Now it is one of the best, if not the best producing farm in Wellington County."

Our analysis of soil samples came in today. Nature has need of us yet. We have helped her, and she has given bounteously; and still, we are just beginning.

CPSIA information can be obtained at www.ICGtesting.com
Printed in the USA
BVOW022251210312

285711BV00003B/82/P